Published in the UK by Scholastic, 2022
1 London Bridge, London, SE1 9BA
Scholastic Ireland, 89E Lagan Road, Dublin Industrial Estate, Glasnevin, Dublin, D11 HP5F

SCHOLASTIC and associated logos are trademarks and/or registered trademarks of Scholastic Inc.

Cover illustration, endpaper and border illustrations by Debby Rahmalia.

Illustrations by Ginnie Hsu, Aaliya Jaheel, Jocelyn Kao, Jen Khatun, Hannah Li, Debby Rahmalia, Abeeha Tariq, KubraTeber, Tika and Tata and Amanda Yoshida.

ISBN 978 07023 1601 2

A CIP catalogue record for this book is available from the British Library.

Printed in the UK by Bell and Bain Ltd, Glasgow
Paper made from wood grown in sustainable forests and other controlled sources.

1 3 5 7 9 10 8 6 4 2

www.scholastic.co.uk

SCHOLASTIC

BEDTIME STORIES

AMAZING Asian Tales FROM THE PAST

WRITTEN BY HANNAH JIANG, SAIMA MIR, SHAE DAVIES, MAISIE CHAN, CYNTHIA SO, ANNABELLE SAMI, BALI RAI, SUFIYA AHMED, REBEKA SHAID AND REKHA WAHEED.

ILLUSTRATED BY AALIYA JALEEL, ABEEHA TARIQ, AMANDA YOSHIDA, DEBBY RAHMALIA, GINNIE HSU, HANNAH LI, JEN KHATUN, JOCELYN KAO, KÜBRA TEBER AND TIKA AND TATA.

CONTENTS

BORROWING ARROWS WITH THATCHED BOATS

BY SEVEN-YEAR-OLD HANNAH JIANG, *FIRST NEWS* COMPETITION WINNER

I'm going to tell you a story about a wise man called Zhuge Liang, who was regarded as one of the most astute people in Chinese history. This is a story full of wisdom and cunning tactics, so please enjoy it with me.

We must start briefly with the period of the Three Kingdoms in ancient China. At that time, China was divided into three kingdoms: Wei, Shu and Wu. Shu and Wu became allies to overthrow the powerful and aggressive Wei. The quick-thinking king of Shu sent his ingenious grand chancellor Zhuge Liang to the kingdom of Wu to cooperate with their general Zhou Yu.

However, Zhou Yu was extremely jealous of Zhuge Liang's shrewdness and political reputation. One day at a camp gathering, Zhou Yu asked Zhuge Liang, **'We are going to war with Wei soon, which method of battle would you recommend?'**

Zhuge Liang gave a sly subtle smile, **'You have the best warships, and you are the greatest general. I'm sure you would agree a battle on the Yangtze River is the best choice.'**

'Yes, I agree with you! But we are short of arrows,' sighed Zhou Yu. **'Everyone admires Mr Zhuge's expertise in crafting tools – could you please make 100,000 arrows for us in ten days?'**

'The war is imminent, so I will get you the 100,000 arrows in three days instead!' Zhuge Liang promised without any hesitation.

Everybody was startled. Zhou Yu was sneakily pleased as he thought it was an impossible task. Zhou Yu requested a signed pledge from Zhuge Liang that if he failed to complete the task, he would face military execution.

Zhou Yu's strategist Lu Su was worried that Zhuge Liang would fail, because he was a friend of Zhuge Liang. Zhuge Liang comforted Lu Su, but he asked for Lu Su's help in getting him twenty boats covered densely with thatch. Each boat should contain thirty soldiers and be packed with thatched dummies on both sides of the boats, and most importantly, it must be kept a secret from Zhou Yu.

Before dawn on the third day, thick fog was floating above the Yangtze River. It rose and spread to fill the whole sky with its endless, grey blanket. Lu Su had arranged everything as requested. Zhuge Liang invited Lu Su, who was still baffled, to board his boat and have tea with him as the twenty boats set off towards the enemy Wei's camp. When they were in shooting distance of their foe's port, Zhuge Liang ordered all the boats to align with their sides facing the enemy. Then, the soldiers lowered all the anchors to keep the boats steady. After that, the soldiers started drumming and shrieked a war cry, pretending an attack was going to take place. Lu Su was worried the enemy would send warships out, but Zhuge Liang assured him that the enemy would never come out in such a foggy condition.

The warlord of Wei, Cao Cao, was deeply suspicious of the attack, and commanded his officer, **'The fog is murky! They want us to go into the river, it must be a trap. Summon six thousand more archers! Shoot their boats down and keep them away from our port!'**

THOCK, THOCK, THOCK went the arrows from the Wei's camp as they hit the thatched boats. Thousands of arrows were raining down from the misty sky and stuck in the thatch. Some missed the boats and splashed into the river like a novice swimmer flapping in the deep end. A soldier informed Zhuge Liang that one side of the boats were too full, and the boats could capsize. Zhuge Liang calmly commanded all the boats to turn around

and use the other side to collect the missiles. Soon, the boat's sides were dense with arrows. As they rowed back home Zhuge Liang asked the soldiers to shout together, **'Thank you, warlord Cao, for your arrows!'** Warlord Cao was furious! Could he take the arrows back?

Zhuge Liang and Lu Su were safely returned. They

collected one hundred and thirty thousand arrows in total! Task completed! Lu Su asked, **'How on earth did you come up with this plan?'**

Zhuge Liang laughed heartily. **'When I took the pledge, I already knew today would be a foggy day and Cao would not dare to fight in such a weather because he is sceptical and suspicious.'**

Lu Su was amazed and admired Zhuge Liang greatly. **'Mr Zhuge is a god!'**

Since Zhuge Liang fulfilled his task beautifully. Zhou Yu couldn't fault him at all, and he was very disappointed! However, this is not the end of the story of this intelligent Zhuge Liang … we'll see you next time!

ILLUSTRATED BY TIKA AND TATA

ROXANA

BY SAIMA MIR

Roxana was the most beautiful girl Alexander had ever seen.

In the fourth century BC, he had marched across the world and conquered most of it, from Greece to the edge of India, but he'd never seen a woman like her.

He watched her from across the hall as she danced gracefully around the room. She looked so different to him, her dark hair flowing down her back, and her skin so golden as if it had been kissed by the sun. She was from Bactria, which would become known as Afghanistan in years to come. Her people looked very different to those of Macedonia, where Alexander had grown up. His complexion was fair, and his hair was like the mane of lion, whose ferocity he shared.

Roxana's father, Oxyartes, noticed him watching his daughter and called her over. **'Come and meet our new king,'** he said. She crossed the room, aware that all eyes were on her.

Alexander the Great, they called him, because he was undefeated in battle. But Roxana wasn't afraid. She knew what people said about her, that she was even more beautiful than the wife of the fallen King Darius, whose country he had just taken.

'Meet my daughter,' said Oxyartes. **'Roxana, my Little Star, would you take His Highness for a walk in the gardens?'**

Roxana smiled and bowed. Alexander had conquered her people, and though she was angry about it, she knew better than to disobey her father. He was a smart man and had his family's best interests at heart. **'Of course, Father,'** she said.

She led the king towards the walled gardens, knowing that his gaze hadn't left her since she arrived. Roxana knew her beauty and her worth; after all, she was the daughter of a nobleman and had led a privileged life at the court of Bessus, who had been king before Alexander.

She had wanted for nothing her entire life. Servants had attended to her every need from the moment she was born. She dined on delicious food, such as grilled meats seasoned and spiced with saffron, and pomegranate and barberry rice filled with almonds and fragrant orange peel.

She wondered if all that was about to change. Women from noble families didn't work in her world. They were raised to be the wives of generals and noblemen, but most of the well-bred men had been killed in war. She had heard that Alexander had asked his soldiers to marry the Bactrian women, but she was not sure how many of the women had done so out of choice.

She ran her fingers over her soft silk gown. The fabric had been imported from China, dyed in bright colours and intricately woven. Now that Bessus was gone, what would become of her family? He had been the chief official in the Persian Empire. After Alexander had invaded Persia and defeated Darius III, Bessus had declared himself king, naming Oxyartes as his chief official.

But that hadn't lasted long, and now he was dead, her father had shifted his allegiance to the man from whom he had defended the mountainous kingdom, and who had killed his friend. She shivered as she remembered what her maid had told her about Bessus's fate.

She glanced at Alexander as they walked through the garden. He was very handsome, and he was being kind to her, but Roxana knew that despite appearances, she and her family were still his captives.

She was a proud woman, and a brave one. She needed to know the truth of who she was dealing with. **'My maid tells me that you chopped off Bessus's nose and ears,'** she said.

Alexander stopped walking. Her bravery surprised him; few dared to speak to him this honestly. He turned towards her, his face solemn.

The air was warm, and the fragrance of feasting and merrymaking filled the air. The moon was full and fat behind him, its light falling on Roxana's face, making her appear even more beautiful. He was equally handsome, with a strong jaw and large eyes.

'It is true,' he said. **'War means doing things that we don't always like.'** He paused and looked at her thoughtfully. **'But I've been thinking that there may be other ways, better ways of building empires. What if I said I had decided to treat your countrymen more honourably?'**

'I would ask what that meant,' she said, choosing her words carefully. She was impressed with his cleverness. She had heard that he had studied with important thinkers, and she herself liked to talk about ideas.

'I want to unite our two races in peace and harmony – the Macedonians and the Persians. But I need your help to do it.'

The work of running the country was left to men, and Roxana had never been asked to be part of something important before. She was flattered, and eager to help, but also keen to make sure her father was safe. 'Whatever you need, I'll do it,' she said, 'if it will mean my family can go free.'

But when Alexander told his men of his proposal, they weren't happy.

'You can't marry her, she is one of our enemies!' said his chief general.

'I can and I shall. I have no need to explain myself to anyone, but as you are my friend, know this: it will make the conquered people happy that I have chosen a wife from among them. It will help us keep our power,' said Alexander.

So it was that Roxana became the queen of a vast empire. But her happiness was short-lived, and soon after the wedding, Alexander marched east to conquer India.

As he had promised, he appointed Roxana's father to a high rank, making him the governor of a region next to India, and her brother was promoted to the elite cavalry.

While her husband was away fighting for more land, Roxana went to live in

Susa, one of the Persian royal capitals. She enjoyed all the luxuries of her childhood and more. She had everything she could dream of, and the Persian people were eager to please her as the wife of their ruler.

But things weren't easy, and the palace needed some work.

'So much of this place is crumbling,' her maidservant said to her one day. **'How long must you stay here?'**

'The palace was built two centuries ago by Darius I,' said Roxana. **'It is an important place, but you're right, it is beginning to show its age. I'm sure Alexander will build me many new palaces when he returns.'**

But when Alexander did return after two years, he had failed to win India. After eight years of fighting, his troops were tired and had refused to go any further. This was the first time he'd been defeated.

He was angry and upset. Instead of building a new palace, in a drunken rage he burned down Persepolis, the other Persian capital – a treasure of the region. Roxana was pregnant at the time, and she had dreamed of handing over the kingdom to her children.

The loss of the learning, art and culture was too great to forgive. **'You destroyed religious works, artworks, tapestries and other priceless cultural artefacts. It was all irreplaceable!'** she said to him. He was full of remorse, but she was too upset to forgive him. Little did she know that as she mourned the loss of Persepolis, she was soon to lose Alexander himself.

A little while later, he developed a fever and died in the ancient city of Babylon, leaving Roxana all alone. It was a dangerous time for women, especially the wife of a dead ruler. Lots of other people wanted to be king. People argued over what to do.

Only Alexander's baby could save Roxana. A son would be king and ensure her safety; a daughter would mean the generals would make Alexander's half-brother Philip king, and Roxana would be killed.

'We need to wait until the baby is born before we decide the future of the empire,' said Perdiccas, one of Alexander's generals. His reasons were selfish. He wanted to keep the empire together, so that he could look after it until the young king was old enough to rule. The other generals did not agree and demanded the empire be divided among them. They fought over it.

Roxana breathed a sigh of relief when the baby was born and it was a boy. **'I'll name him Alexander IV,'** she said. **'I must plan his future, and make sure no one takes his throne.'** To do this, she decided to get rid of some of her rivals. Her husband had taken a second wife, a woman called Stateira. She was the daughter of Darius III and of royal blood. Worried that Stateira may also be pregnant and steal her son's throne, Roxana had her killed.

But things were still tricky. Alexander IV wasn't yet old enough to rule. All decisions were made by Perdiccas, who commanded Alexander's top regiment, the Companions. When Perdiccas died, the generals began to quarrel again, and it looked like this time there would be a war between them.

Roxana was a clever woman, and she escaped to a place called Pella to live with Olympias, her husband's mother.

Soon after, Alexander IV was declared the undisputed king. Roxana and Olympias ruled for him until he reached an age where he was old enough to make decisions about the empire.

Roxana breathed a sigh of relief. She missed the ease and luxuries of the court at Susa. Few people spoke Persian, and the food was bland, but she and her son were safe.

She planned a feast to celebrate their safety. She called over cooks and maids from the city where she'd grown up, and asked them to prepare a delicious meal of grilled meats and all the fragrant foods that she had grown up with. Her son sat beside her, tucking into berries and rice flavoured with herbs and spices.

Within hours they were dead. They'd been poisoned. A general named Cassander, who hated Alexander the Great and all his family, had wanted the throne for himself, and he had taken it.

From nobleman's daughter to the wife of the great Alexander, and queen of the world's largest empire, mother of his heir, ruler of Greece, prisoner and once again mother of the king, Roxana had achieved a great deal in her thirty years of life.

ILLUSTRATED BY ABEEHA TARIQ

JULIA DOMNA

BY SAIMA MIR

Scholars, poets and philosophers sat around the Great Hall of the Imperial Palace, surrounded by the impressive ceremonies that happened at royal events. Their empress had fought and won a mighty legal battle. They dined on fragrant fruits, honey and cheese, wondering about the endless possibilities of the universe. At their centre sat Empress Julia Domna, discussing religious ideas, the Roman Empire and what lay ahead.

She was tired from the events of the last few weeks. But she was a clever woman, and knew not to show her enemies her true feelings. There were many such enemies at court.

As she listened to her guests, she thought back to her childhood and how far she'd come. **'She has a mind like mercury,'** her tutor had said to her father when she was a little girl.

Her intelligence had inspired many stories, and these tales led to the

ambitious army officer Septimius Severus asking for her hand in marriage when she was only sixteen. Septimius would soon become emperor.

Julia had first met Septimius when he came to the city of Emesa to honour Elagabal, the sun god. He hadn't made much of an impression on the ten-year-old Julia back then. Her life was full of the usual fun things of a girl her age, and she had little interest in marriage.

Being the daughter of the high priest of Elagabal, Julia lived close to the temple with her family. It was the centre of worship for the cult of the sun god, and countless pilgrims came from all over the region to offer prayers. They'd ask for money, for children, for happiness and for love. Septimius came searching for all this and more. After they married, he would often tell her of how he had heard tales of a girl in the East whose horoscope said she was destined to be a king's wife.

But even without the prophecy, Julia had made quite an impression on the centurion, and he never forgot her. When his wife died, he came back to Emesa in search of her. Her father, Julius Bassianus, readily accepted the proposal.

She still remembered the day of her marriage as if it were yesterday. **'I'm going to write great literary works!'** she'd told her mother that morning.

'Women don't get to do such things,' her mother had said to her. **'You'll be far too busy for such frivolity.'**

'Then I shall inspire and encourage others,' she'd said.

As Septimius kissed her and presented her with a ring, as was custom, her heart filled with dreams. **'The third finger of the left hand is thought to be connected to the heart,'** he'd said as he slipped the ring onto her slender finger. She was excited at the prospect of her new life.

As she sat in the imperial court, listening to Philostratus, she knew she'd achieved what she'd set out to do. **'Thank you, Empress, for encouraging my work. I'm working on the seventh volume of *The Life of Apollonius Tyana*. I hope to show it to you soon.'**

Julia was not only the wife of Septimius, but also the mother of two grown children. Her eldest son, Bassianus, who everyone now called Caracalla, was the apple of her eye, and her younger son, Geta, was vivacious and full of life.

She touched her wavy hair, making sure it still covered her ears and that the chignon at the back was still neat. She was worried it was starting to thin, but she was lucky enough to have a team of ornatrices to create elaborate hairstyles.

Being the wife of the Roman emperor came with certain perks, such as the endless gifts brought to her by guests. **'Frankincense and myrrh for Augusta Julia Domna,'** said one of the guests, holding out two small glass bottles. He bowed low as he spoke. This queen surpassed all others. She was loved by her people, and she was concerned about their welfare. For a woman to take part in the actual running of the empire was rare. Men were usually in charge, and women were considered their possessions. That Julia came from his homeland made him very proud. **'I too come from Emesa,'** he said.

Julia smiled at him; the presence of someone from her childhood at court filled her with warmth. But ruling an empire was not for the faint-hearted, and there were many close by who would harm her. She handed the vials to one of her slaves. **'I hope you understand if my servant tries the perfume first? These are difficult times.'**

Plans to usurp Julia Domna were always whispered of. She'd only just fended off such an attempt with her wisdom and knowledge. That was also the reason for this grand celebration.

The maidservant carefully inhaled the vapours, declaring them safe and passing them back to her queen.

Julia took the bottle from her servant, and the fragrance filled her senses, taking her back to the marketplace of her childhood.

'The incense used to be carried on camel caravans from the Yemen,' she said to the young poet. **'You have taken me back to my youth.'**

That night, Julia dreamed of her homeland. All around her, stalls had been piled high with fruits and vegetables, along with fresh breads baked from the wheat that was plentiful in the area.

She thought back to the chants of the priests, many of whom she knew, coming from the traditional family that she did. It was such an honour to be part of the family responsible for worshipping the great sun god. She had often stood barefoot in the temple asking Elagabal for countless things.

The hustle and bustle of the pilgrims made the market swell like the River Orontes, which blessed them with its bounty. The pilgrims also brought money with them, which they spent in the city, and were responsible for the region's prosperity.

Julia saw herself walking slowly through the market, lifting her robes to avoid the dusty streets, and then her dream changed, becoming louder, brighter, and she saw herself entering the city of Rome alongside her two sons. All around them men and women cheered at the glorious spectacle that was her husband's victory march to become emperor.

She woke with a jolt, relieved to find herself alone in her chambers. She found it difficult to sleep these days. The trial that had been orchestrated by her husband's top adviser, Plautianus, had drained her of joy. That Septimius had doubted her loyalty to the point that he had accused her of treason had broken her heart.

She had recognized Plautianus's designs when he first came to court – there was something about the way he looked at her – but Septimius hadn't believed her. Instead, he had handed more and more power to the man, until he became the Praetorian Prefect, with control over the running of the empire, the money and the judicial systems.

The power had gone to his head. Despite receiving honours reserved for members of the imperial family, he had been jealous of Julia. She sometimes wondered if this had been her husband's plan, to make sure that she didn't get too powerful while he was away from court.

Somehow Plautianus had persuaded Septimius that his wife was having an affair.

She would never forget the day he had called for her to come to court. She had put down her fabrics and pins immediately. She knew that if she resisted, the soldiers would take her by force. She'd heard whispers that this was coming, but nothing can prepare an empress for public arrest.

She shuddered as she remembered how she stood alone before the magistrate as the case against her was read.

'The lady is accused of having a relationship with another man. As she is the wife of the emperor, this means she has committed treason,' said Plautianus.

The trial had been long and arduous, taking its toll on Julia, but never one to back down from a fight, she had used her fierce intelligence and knowledge of the law to her advantage. Eventually, the magistrate had decided that she was innocent.

Though this trial was over, others were not. The plot to make her look bad and turn her family against her went on.

Later that night, she lay in bed remembering how things were when her children were small. How they had played together, running after each other and wrestling in the courtyard of the palace. But their play fighting had turned real with time, and she was worried they would hurt each other. She climbed out of her bed, walking to her dresser to take a sip of water. She was so restless. Her eyes fell on her jewellery box. She lifted the lid of the clay pot. Inside were large gold coins with **'IVLIA DOMNA'** written on them, in honour of the conqueror's wife – in honour of her. As prophesized, she had indeed become the wife of a king.

But the priests who drew up the horoscopes had failed to warn her of the dangers and consequences of that, and now court life had become distasteful to her.

She decided she would withdraw from much of it, and spend her time learning and reading.

There was a knock at the door, and her son, Caracalla entered.

'Is your brother here too?' she said. He shook his head.

'I wish the two of you would get along,' she said sadly, turning back to her jewellery box and closing it. But she knew they never would. This was how things were in political empires; families turned on each other for the throne.

'I wanted to see how you were,' he said. **'We didn't get chance to speak at the convivium.'**

'Thank you,' she said, hugging him tightly, before letting him go and taking a long look at him.

She couldn't believe how tall he was now, that she was the mother of two grown men.

She thought about Plautilla, the daughter of Plautianus, and a plan formed in her mind. Wasn't marriage between feuding families how royalty had maintained control for centuries? Maybe there was time for one last plan. **'You are ready to get married, Caracalla,'** she said, and proceeded to tell him of her designs.

GLOSSARY

Caravan – a large group of people, with vehicles or animals, travelling together in a single line

Convivium – a banquet in Roman times

Court – a place where legal cases are heard

Horoscope – a forecast of someone's future, based on the positions of the stars and planets at the time of that person's birth

Judicial – decided in or coming from a court of law

Praetorian Prefect – the commander of the praetorian guard, the bodyguards of the Roman emperor

ILLUSTRATED BY KÜBRA TEBER

THE TRƯNG SISTERS

BY SHAE DAVIES

Two small girls run to the entrance of the Hai Ba temple in Hanoi, Vietnam. Their laughs echo down the street and their grandmother chides them for being so loud.

'Do you know why we have come here?' the old woman asks, attempting to regain their focus.

The youngest shakes her head. The eldest raises her hand fast and high in the air like an excited schoolgirl. Her grandmother nods at her to speak.

'This week is the Hai Ba Trung Temple Festival!' she exclaims.

'Yes, Lễ Hội Hai Bà Trưng ,' their grandmother smiles, repeating its name in Vietnamese.

Hai Ba means **'two ladies'**, and the temple, like the festival, is in honour of two brave sisters that led Vietnam to victory!

'**Come,**' their grandmother says, taking a seat. The girls eagerly follow; they love to hear her speak. '**Let me tell you the story of the Trung sisters.**'

*

Long, long ago, in AD 14, there was a beautiful country called the Kingdom of Nam Việt, or what you may now know as Vietnam. Nam Việt was bright and beautiful. It was a place where the sun shone on the crops and the people lived off the land in peace and harmony.

However, Nam Việt and China had been bitter rivals for a very long time. In 111 BC (a very long time ago!), the Han defeated the last ruler of the Nam Việt Triệu Dynasty and tried to take over the whole country.

Nam Việt was split into several Chinese provinces. In AD 34 the Chinese appointed a new governor called Su Ding (which in Vietnamese is Tô Định, which means '**to rule the whole**').

New Vietnamese leaders were chosen to look after the provinces and report back to the Chinese. The Vietnamese leaders stood up to the Chinese as much as they could, but Chinese rule grew harsher and harsher as the years went on.

One of these leaders was a general, and he looked after the Giao Chỉ district (now known as Northern Vietnam). This district was quiet, so the Chinese did not watch it carefully, and this gave the Vietnamese some freedom.

The general had two beautiful and brave daughters that he loved dearly. Trưng Trắc and Trưng Nhị were his only children and would one day inherit his titles and land.

Trưng Trắc liked puzzles and grew up to be a master planner, while Trưng Nhị liked to play fight and became known as a fearless warrior.

The Trưng sisters studied hard, learning Chinese literature and martial arts with their father.

As the sisters grew, they witnessed more cruelty. The Chinese killed anyone who didn't agree with their rules. They tried to stop women inheriting land and made people pay very high taxes.

When their father died, the two girls were left in pain, with a burning desire to carry out his legacy and his vision for a free Nam Việt.

During this time, in traditional Vietnamese society, women had more rights than many women in Asia or Europe. They were free to own property, and they could become political leaders, judges, traders or even warriors. But To Dinh did not like this, and he wanted to take this away from Vietnamese women.

But the Trưng sisters' mother, Lady Man Thiện, did not care for the Chinese rules, going against them when she chose not to marry again. She focused all her energy on training her daughters in the art of war – teaching them military strategy, martial arts, bow fighting and sword fighting!

One day, Trưng Trắc fell in love with a strong and kind man from a neighbouring town and the two soon married. His name was Thi Sach and he was the governor of the Châu Diên district. Thi Sach was brave, and just like the sisters, he dreamed of overthrowing the Chinese.

When the Chinese raised the taxes again, Thi Sach decided to take a stand. He met with the governor to discuss the matter.

'To Dinh, please stop, the people do not deserve this.'

The governor smiled a cruel and knowing smile, then lifted his hand and gestured to his guards, who dragged Thi Sach away by the arms. He was arrested and killed.

When Trưng Trắc heard the news, she was heartbroken. But more importantly, she was furious. The fire inside her grew, and she found strength in her fury. She chose not to take the traditional period of mourning, and instead threw herself into her plot for revenge.

In the book where she kept her poems, her pen struck the page and wrote the words that echoed throughout Vietnam for years to come:

**Foremost, I will avenge my country,
Second, I will restore the Hung lineage.
Third, I will avenge the death of my husband,
Lastly, I vow that these goals will be accomplished.**

Trưng Nhị ran into the room, having just heard the news. She took her sister's hand and looked into her eyes and nodded. No more words were passed, but they knew that this was the moment they had been preparing for all their lives.

For 150 years no one in Nam Việt had had the courage to stand up to the Chinese – until the Trưng sisters!

Together they organized civil war. They gained support from nearby tribal lords and recruited nobles from among the Lac people as well as landlords and farmers, searching high and low for others who opposed the Chinese.

There were many among the Vietnamese who did not think women should be leaders and doubted the sisters could win the war. The sisters knew what to do to show them they were wrong.

'You do not think women should be leaders?' Trưng Trắc called into the crowd, taking out a knife. The brave sisters ran into the forest to hunt a tiger that had been attacking local farmers. Soon they returned with the tiger's blood on their faces. They'd done it! After that, many men were convinced to join their cause.

Together they created a peasant army of 80,000 people. This army was made up of many women, including thirty-six female generals, which was very rare at the time.

The sisters marched forward to the capital, the two of them sitting on top of huge elephants.

First the sisters took the town of Luy Lâu, and within months they had taken over sixty-five cities!

By AD 40, To Dinh did not have much territory left. The Chinese Han Emperor, Guangwu, heard more and more tales of the sister's bravery, and he sat in the capital feeling terrified.

Eventually, they reached their final battle and defeated To Dinh. Nam Việt was free!

The Trưng sisters ruled Nam Việt themselves from their capital at Mê Linh.

They chased away all the horrible Chinese governors and bureaucrats, and put the terrible Han taxes in the bin.

They created a new nation from Southern Vietnam into Southern China, and a new government that followed traditional Vietnamese values.

And so, the sisters ruled the land in peace and harmony, for three amazing years.

Until one day, they lost it all.

Emperor Guangwu wanted to take Nam Việt back, and secretly formed a new army to do exactly that. In AD 43, China invaded Nam Việt under the command of general Ma Yuan. He had 8,000 experienced soldiers and 12,000 militiamen!

The sisters fought bravely at Lãng Bạc (near what is now known as Hanoi), but the Chinese soldiers defeated the sisters. Most of their army deserted, and the sisters escaped, but they soon lost another battle at Hát Môn (near modern-day Son Tay).

Not wanting to be captured and humiliated by the Chinese, the sisters sadly drowned themselves.

*

'And even though the sisters were defeated, many rebellions followed that, a lot of them led by women! Soldiers carried pictures of the sisters into battle to give them strength. They gave Nam Việt a taste of independence.' The girls' grandmother raised her hands into the sky dramatically, and the girls giggled, copying her.

'**They became national heroines,**' she said, smiling. '**Especially in 939, when Vietnam finally became independent from China!**'

'**Yay!**' the little girls shouted as they ran around waving their arms. Their grandmother chided them again for being so loud.

'**Come girls, let us send a prayer to the Trung Sisters.**' She nodded at the temple and the three of them walked towards it.

*

Although nearly two thousand years ago now, the sister's courage and sacrifice are celebrated every year, their story passed from one generation to another. Stories, songs, plays and monuments have all been inspired by their brave tale. It is said that they were worshipped like goddesses, and many believed that if you prayed to them it would bring rain – maybe because of their watery death!

It is believed that if the sisters had not stood up and inspired their people to rebel against the Chinese, there would be no Vietnam today.

GLOSSARY

Han people – an East Asian ethnic group native to China
General – an officer of high military rank
Lac people – people who lived in what is now North Vietnam
Martial arts – sports that originated mainly in Japan, Korea and China as forms of self-defence, such as judo and karate
Militiamen – a group of trained people who are not soldiers but can serve as members of the military in an emergency

ILLUSTRATED BY GINNIE HSU

XUANZANG

THE MONK WHO COLLECTED MANUSCRIPTS

BY MAISIE CHAN

Xuanzang sat cross-legged, straightened his spine and took a deep breath in and out. The thirteen-year-old knew that times in China were different now the Tang Dynasty had taken over. The new regime brought with it much unrest, and to add to the strife his father had recently passed away, leaving young Xuanzang in his gege's care. His brother was called Changjie and was a Buddhist monk. Changjie had taken it upon himself to teach his younger sibling how to meditate, to help him cope with such huge changes to the family and the world at large.

'**Do you think this will work?**' Xuanzang said, trying hard not to open his eyes. As a beginner, sitting still was not easy. His brother, on the other hand, had many years of training. Meditating now came easily to Changjie.

'**Give it some time. With practice you will become much better at it, and soon it will be like breathing itself,**' Changjie said, reassuringly. '**Baba is gone now, but with all of his years working for the emperor and following the** ways on Confucius, he was not one to sit still for long either!'

'I can do it! I know it!' Xuanzang said. 'I'm not like Baba, I'm more like you!'

'Family is wonderful, and even though Baba believed in Confucian ways, which say that family is the foundation of society, I believe that the Buddhist scriptures and mediation can help everyone,' Changjie said.

Xuanzang thought that his brother was wise, and soon enough he found himself eager to sit in stillness. He realized that it made him feel calm and good about life.

'I want to learn about how to be a monk, just like you!' Xuanzang told his older brother.

'If you walk on the path, then you will find yourself.' Changjie said. Xuanzang was happy to begin his journey into Buddhism.

*

In 618, a civil war broke out where they lived in Henan, and the brothers decided to take refuge in Sichuan. They spent three years in a monastery studying the Buddhist texts, and in 622 Xuanzang become an ordained Buddhist monk. One of the things that Xuanzang loved the most was reading the scriptures. He studied all that he could get his hands on. However, something was not quite right.

'I read these scriptures repeatedly, but sometimes they don't make sense. They tell you one thing and then contradict the thing that they just said! The meaning isn't always clear.'

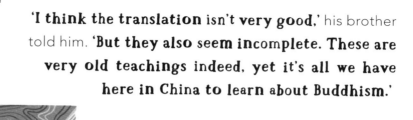

'I think the translation isn't very good,' his brother told him. 'But they also seem incomplete. These are very old teachings indeed, yet it's all we have here in China to learn about Buddhism.'

'It feels wrong. I can't carry on with my studies when I feel like what I am reading isn't right. I need to go to India and find out for myself what the real teachings are. I will make the journey and bring back scriptures to translate.'

'That is such a long way to go, and you will have to learn Sanskrit, the sacred original language of the scriptures. It could take you a long time to understand it. Are you sure, little brother?' Changjie said.

'Yes! I feel like it is my calling,' Xuanzang said. 'Do you give me your blessing?'

'Of course. Go on your journey, and I look forward to when you return,' Changjie said.

However, there was a big problem. The Emperor Taizong forbade Xuanzang to travel to India and would not give him a travel permit. Xuanzang had to make a choice: stay and be forever displeased with what he was reading or go under the night sky and follow his heart's true desire.

There was only one thing for it. Xuanzang felt it was his destiny. *I must go on this journey, though it will take many years. I must travel to the home of Buddhism in India and learn more about the religion which has given me so much.*

'You are very brave to go under these circumstances,' his brother told him. 'Without the Emperor's blessing you will be seen as a fugitive and a law-breaker.'

'I'll write to you, dear gege,' Xuanzang said, and he slipped out of the city under the cover of night. Xuanzang bade his brother farewell, and under the shadowy cloak of darkness with only the moon's light to guide him, he slipped past the guards and made his way to India.

*

Luckily for Xuanzang, the Silk Road had been established as a route where merchants could import and export their wares. It could also be used for those who wished to see other countries and to explore. It was this route that Xuanzang followed, travelling with merchant caravans into Central Asia. Xuanzang was a curious monk; he loved to see new sights and smell new foods. He relished the idea of expanding his knowledge of the world and the people in it. However, he was abandoned by his companions somewhere around the Gobi Desert.

'What shall I do now?' he exclaimed. But Xuanzang was not a person to give up easily, and he decided to go on alone. If he was heading in the right direction, he would be fine, he thought.

In one dry oasis town, a Buddhist king called Qu Wentai of Turfan wanted Xuanzang to stay and teach Buddhism there – forever! Xuanzang wasn't willing to spend his whole life in one place working for the king, so he made a deal to come back to Turfan and teach for three years on his way back to China. The king agreed and Xuanzang went on his way.

And so further on he went, towards Tashkent, meeting people who were very different to the Chinese people back home, with new and exciting foods to try. However, when he reached the Pamir mountain range, things became tricky. The rough terrain and treacherous weather around the mountains was difficult for him to navigate. The snow-topped mountains looked majestic from a distance, but for the monk on his pilgrimage it was terrifying. The freezing temperatures and unfamiliar terrain almost killed him.

Dear Brother, my fingers are trembling from the cold. I don't know if I will survive the harsh conditions here. Only with the will of Buddha will we know. I am lost as all around me is white with snow, and I fear I may not reach my destination.

However, Xuanzang did survive.

Nearing his destination, Xuanzang felt centred; his Buddhist training and practice had helped him make the journey. When he reached the kingdom of Gandhara, Xuanzang took a ship down the River Ganges to Mathura, the heart of Buddhism in northern India.

Xuanzang saw habits that were not common in China. He wrote to his brother and told him about all of the new things he had seen.

Dear Brother, things are very different here. Yesterday, we travelled to a nearby village where a huge elephant used its long trunk to pick the daintiest of flowers! I couldn't believe my eyes. Such a huge beast could stomp on a man and kill him instantly, and yet it could be so gentle in the moment with a beautiful flower. Brother, I wish you were here to see such wonders.

I spend all morning in meditation. And in the afternoons and evenings I have classes in the language of the scriptures. By learning the language myself, I will be able to tell the true meaning of the scriptures in their entirety. It will make such a difference to our knowledge of Buddhism.

The smell of this place tickles my nostrils; they cook with spices that we have never seen. It helps the gut to fight off illness. The local people are very kind and offer us food when we pass. I am excited to keep working on the teachings I have found, and when I return I shall be able to pass them on through my words.

The halls are full of students, eager to learn, just like me. Even though there are many students who have come here from all over the world, you can still find stillness when meditating. Not only are there the teachings of Buddhism here, but the greatest minds have also come here to share their wisdom on things such as mathematics and medicine. I will return when I am satisfied that I have gained enough knowledge to share with Buddhists in China. Until then, dear brother, I bid you farewell.

In 645, Xuanzang decided to return to China. He did return to teach in Turfan on his way home, as he had promised the king. The remainder of his trip home took him just two years. He had been gone for sixteen long years, and in that time had written down his experiences of life in India and of his travels. He had learned a new language and had spent many years translating the Buddhist scriptures into Chinese. His arrival in Chang'an was met with much jubilation as a large crowd of well-wishers came out to greet him. He was summoned to see the Emperor Taizong, the one who had previously refused him a travel permit. Taizong loved hearing about the far-off places and unusual experiences that Xuanzang had faced. He became a national hero, and the emperor offered him a job as an imperial minister.

But Xuanzang knew from an early age that he did not wish to follow in the footsteps of his father and had devoted his life to Buddhism. He was not about to change that path now.

HISTORICAL NOTE

Xuanzang's writings became the bedrock of Chinese Buddhism, and his teachings even travelled to Japan, where Xuanzang's scriptures and his ideas were also a big influence. Even though Xuanzang had brought back hundreds of new manuscripts, he only managed to translate seventy-five of them before he died in 664! The job was too much even for him.

Xuanzang wrote an account of his epic journey called the *Datang-Xiyu-Ji* (**'The Records of the Western Regions of the Tang Empire'**), and his tales inspired the most famous Chinese novel ever – *Journey to the West* by Wu Cheng'en. Xuanzang's legacy remains today all over China, where Buddhism is one of the most popular religions.

GLOSSARY

Baba – father

Buddhism – a religion or philosophy from Asia, founded in the sixth century BC by Siddartha Gautama (The Buddha)

Confucius – a Chinese philosopher from the sixth century BC

Gege – older brother

Meditation – the action of meditating – focusing your mind for a period of time, in silence or with the aid of chanting

Merchant caravan – a group of traders travelling together

Oasis – a sheltered watering hole and resting place in a desert

Ordained – a formally recognized priest, rabbi, minister or other religious role

Tang Dynasty – a golden age of Chinese arts and culture, from AD 618 to 906

ILLUSTRATED BY HANNAH LI

MURASAKI SHIKIBU

BY CYNTHIA SO

Murasaki Shikibu, who was born in Heian-kyō, then the capital of Japan, around the year 973, is the author of one of the world's first novels.

But Murasaki Shikibu is not her real name. Murasaki, which means **'violet'**, is the name of one of the characters in her book. And Shikibu is taken from the name of the place her father worked, the Ministry of Ceremonies. We don't know her real name, so we will have to call her by the name the world knows her by.

*

There was a big and powerful family in Japan called the Fujiwara clan. The most important people in the family basically controlled the country at the time, but Murasaki belonged to a minor branch of it.

Her father was a scholar of the Chinese classics. When Murasaki was little, she would sit in on her brother's Chinese lessons. And she was riveted! She was very lucky to be able to learn such things by listening to her brother, as in traditional Heian culture, girls were only supposed to learn music, Japanese poetry and calligraphy. She discovered her love for both Chinese and Japanese poetry, and she couldn't get enough of reading. She inhaled texts like air, and she was much faster at learning than her brother, who would frown at her and make faces, obviously annoyed at her abilities.

'Stop showing off about how you can understand the stuff I can't!' he huffed. **'Father isn't even supposed to teach you Chinese. It's for boys.'**

Her eyes welling up with tears, she ran to her father and cried, **'Daddy, look how much I read today! Brother doesn't like it, but I think he's just jealous that I'm smarter than him.'**

His father didn't beam at her like she wanted him to. In fact, he shook his head and sighed. **'If only you had been my son and not my daughter,'** he said. **'Then I could be proud of you!'**

Murasaki realized then that she was not what society expected her to be. But this did not stop her from being who she was.

*

Murasaki was still not married in her mid-twenties. This was uncommon for noblewomen at the time; she was aware of girls in her huge family getting married much younger. She had a suitor called Nobutaka, a man who wanted her to be his wife, but she wasn't sure what she thought of him.

When her father was sent to be governor of Echizen province, he asked

Murasaki, **'Would you like to come with me?'** Echizen was five days' travel from the capital, Heian-Kyō (modern-day Kyoto), where they lived. Murasaki had never heard of women travelling that far. **'I know it's unusual,'** her father said. **'But you're an unusual woman.'**

Murasaki decided to go with him.

It was colder in Echizen than back home. It snowed more often, and it was lonelier too. Women were not allowed a great deal of freedom and tended to stay indoors most of the time, but even so, there were plenty more things to do and people to see in the bustling capital. She didn't think she would mind the quiet – she was quite an introvert, and she appreciated having the time to read and be alone with her thoughts. But still, she started looking forward to Nobutaka's letters, which he sent regularly. In the chill of winter, his words were warm.

'Father, what do you think of me going back to Heian-Kyo and marrying Nobutaka?' she asked one day.

'It's up to you,' her father said. **'You are not a woman who will let others' opinions affect what you do, are you?'**

She nodded.

The next day, shivering in her frosty room, she reread Nobutaka's letters and thought for a long time. Finally, she wrote to him: *I will return to the capital and marry you.*

And that's what she did.

Only three short years later, Nobutaka died. A plague had swept through the city and taken his life. He had left Murasaki with a daughter – a small toddler, who had only just learned to walk.

Murasaki wept. **'What will happen to me now that my husband is gone?'** she asked the empty air.

She buried herself in writing and read her poems out loud to her daughter, though she knew the words would not mean anything to such a tiny child. The melodic sounds of the poetry seemed to calm her daughter like sweet little lullabies.

In the night, when her daughter was fast asleep, Murasaki would look up at the moon and characters' voices would come to her, whispering. She wrote down snippets, which turned into chapters. In the morning she would look over her scribbles and be surprised by the richness of the story that was emerging. **'This isn't just a poem, or a collection of poems,'** she remarked to herself. **'It's going to be something much more than that. I have to keep writing!'**

As she wrote, she started to care about her main character as though he were her second child. He was a real, breathing person to her, not just some lines on a page. His name was Hikaru

Genji – **'the Shining One'.** Genji was the illegitimate son of an emperor, and he had lots of love affairs with noblewomen at court.

Murasaki could see Genji's life unfolding in front of her, a long and winding path. He was going to be exiled by the emperor as punishment for his brazen behaviour, but he would eventually find his way back to court. But all that had not happened yet. It would take many more pages, and many more years to write.

Murasaki shared the early chapters with her friends and family, who adored every last word. **'We can't wait for more,'** they would say. **'When's the next bit coming?'**

Her family, as we've mentioned, was a big and powerful one. It wasn't long before word of her literary talent reached an influential relative of hers called Michinaga, whose young daughter, Shoshi, was the emperor's wife. Michinaga was the real power behind the throne.

'Murasaki must come to the palace and be Shoshi's lady-in-waiting,' Michinaga said. **'She will be a wonderful tutor and companion for my daughter, and she can continue writing her book with our support. I'm confident that** *The Tale of Genji* **will soon be the talk of the town, and Murasaki will be the star of Shoshi's court!'**

Securing such a prestigious position was a relief for Murasaki, who had been so worried about her role in society since her husband's death. But upon her arrival at the palace, she quickly realized that she didn't fit in there, just as she had never really fit in anywhere else the rest of her life. She started to keep a diary, where she would pour out her feelings.

'How can it be that I'm in the royal palace, the glittering heart of the country, surrounded by people and culture, and feel lonelier than I have ever been?' she pondered.

There were other female writers at court, but she didn't get along with any of them. Was it because they were in competition with one another, each striving to prove themselves to be the best, to win the attention of everyone at court? Perhaps. But still. 'They're all so arrogant!' she shouted to nobody in the silence of her room, frustrated at her own inability to make friends. 'And they're trying way too hard to be clever!'

But in the end, she knew what the real problem was. She just wasn't good at being sociable. She couldn't hold a witty conversation. She didn't laugh at the same jokes that other people thought were funny. She was awkward and shy, and she loved books and poetry more than people. While others were enjoying themselves at parties, she spent all her time daydreaming about stories.

'It's fine,' Murasaki told herself. 'It doesn't matter what people think of me. I'll just throw myself into my writing.'

So she did. She kept working hard on *The Tale of Genji*, packing it full of details about life at court, drawn from her own experiences. It grew and grew. As soon as she finished one chapter, it would be devoured by all the ladies at court, and even all the men, and Murasaki's heart would glow with pride. Then everyone would clamour for the next chapter, and Murasaki would go back to her writing desk and sink into the world she was creating, forgetting about the world she lived in.

*

The Tale of Genji ended up being fifty-four books long, with a cast of some four hundred characters. Even though there were so many characters, Murasaki managed to keep track of them all, and made sure that they were consistent throughout the story. She carried on writing this masterpiece all her life. It is the first Japanese novel, one of the first novels in the world, and also one of the longest, and it was written by a brilliant woman who was never what other people expected her to be, but who always tried her best to stay true to herself.

GLOSSARY

Court – the home of the ruler of a country and of the important people who live and work there

Introvert – a shy person

Novel – a long fiction book

Plague – a disease that spreads quickly

ILLUSTRATED BY JOCELYN KAO

SORGHAGHTANI BEKI

BY ANNABELLE SAMI

MY STORY

Have you ever heard of a vast country in East Asia, sandwiched between China and Russia? It's called Mongolia, and I was born there more than eight hundred years ago. When I look over the rolling grassland plains and snow-capped mountains of the countryside, it's easy to forget that so much time has passed since I lived there. But when I see the soaring skyscrapers in the capital city of Ulaanbaatar, I like to reflect on the part I played in ensuring the success and development of my country.

So I'd like to tell you my story, if you'll listen, of how I went from being the daughter of a minor chieftain to one of the most influential women in the Mongol Empire.

I was known as many things during my life: princess, mother, trusted advisor. Even now after my life has ended, I live on in a different way… But first let me take you back to the beginning – Mongolia in the twelfth century. Where my story begins.

LIFE AS A NOMAD

I always loved my country, even as a child. I knew the lush grasslands just as well as an old friend, and my companions and I often rode our horses there. But merchants who returned after travelling on the Silk Road trading route would tell us tales about the sweltering sands in the Gobi desert and the endless starlit skies. I felt amazed that our country could contain such different landscapes and be home to so many different tribes. My uncle was the leader of our tribe, the Keraites, and my father was a chieftain, giving me my first identity in life as a princess. But being a princess didn't mean I lived in some majestic fairy-tale castle with butlers and maids. Oh no! My people were nomads, moving from place to place according to the seasons, raising our livestock on the land and transporting only what was necessary.

We carried everything with us – even our houses!

Home to me was our settlement of round goat-felt yurts, standing strong against the flat, green plains called the steppes. I can still smell the smoke of the burning wood as the stove inside the yurt was fired up on frosty mornings.

If only life could have been as peaceful as the yaks seemed, grazing and snoozing on the grass all day long. But the many powerful tribes of Mongolia were often at war with each other. Men would go to fight and not return. It was a scary and uncertain time for all of us. But that changed when Temüjin came along. Tales of his exploits were carried on the wind to us from across the land. With a combination of violence, bargaining and alliances, he was uniting the tribes of Mongolia under his power. I still remember my uncle's and father's worried expressions when they realized our tribe was next.

After uniting all the tribes of Mongolia, Temüjin was elected Great Khan in 1207, and I knew things would change forever. Of course, you now know

Temüjin by a different name – the fierce conqueror Genghis Khan.

A WOMAN'S PLACE

As Genghis Khan brought great change to the world, so too he brought huge change to my life. I knew that when he brought the Keraites under his rule, Genghis Khan would require something from us to solidify the bonds between his family and ours. The day came quicker than I expected. I fought the urge to run as fast as I could to the Altai mountains and never return. My father informed me that I was to be given as a bride to Genghis Khan's youngest son, Tolui. We were both only thirteen. When I finally met the man who was supposed to be my husband, he looked just as scared as me, and just as young. But I felt comfort knowing that we were both scared teenagers, in this together.

AN AMBITIOUS MOTHER AND WIFE

As I grew into an adult, I watched the Mongol Empire spread to lands I could never have dreamed of as a child. Genghis Khan's violent conquests meant that, at its biggest, the Mongol Empire stretched all the way from the sea of Japan to Eastern Europe. As our empire grew, so did my ambition. As Tolui's wife, I had more power and responsibility than I ever would as a chieftain's daughter. Of course, I wasn't the only woman in my husband's life … he had over seven wives and concubines! That may sound shocking, but in my time this was normal. And for my intelligence and capability, I was Tolui's favourite.

After Genghis Khan's death my husband was given rule over the homelands of Mongolia, a huge responsibility that took much work. I remember many long nights sitting around the iron stove in our yurt, Tolui fretting over some issue that I would calmly suggest the solution to. Only then, once he'd listened to my advice, would the deep line in-between his eyebrows soften. I was not just a wife to him, but an advisor.

Although I knew I was making a difference by helping to run a part of the empire, I still knew I had bigger ambitions than this. It was only in 1209 when I became a mother that I realized how to truly leave my mark.

I had four sons. The eldest was Mongke, followed by Kublai, Hulagu and Ariq. That was four opportunities to be the mother of a great ruling khan! I knew that we had been given a miracle and I could not waste it. I had to raise them properly and prepare them to be future leaders. The role of mother was to be my greatest role yet.

The first thing I did was to make sure that my sons could speak the many different languages of the surrounding regions. A khan should be able to speak the languages of his subjects, especially as the empire had expanded to many different countries. I also made sure that my sons' wives could read and write in Mongolian. I myself was illiterate, and I always felt frustrated that others had to read out important documents to me. My sons' wives would not have the same fate. After all, a strong wife makes a strong ruler. I also raised my sons in the Nestorian faith – the Church of the East. Although in the Mongol Empire the state was more important than religion, our beliefs were very tolerant of other religions. Growing up, my sons saw me provide charity to both Christians and Muslims. This meant that they would grow up to be leaders tolerant of the many different religions that existed within the empire.

All was going to plan … until 1232. After twenty-eight years of marriage, my husband Tolui died at the age of forty-one. That day, I sat and prayed for hours, asking for the strength to carry on. I had no time to mourn and I would not let this stop my sons from gaining their rightful places as khans.

Ambition drove me through the darkest days of grief. Losing my husband did not have to mean losing power.

A LADY MOST RENOWNED

My goal of ensuring my sons all rose to power was still at the forefront of my mind as I navigated the next chapter of my life without Tolui. I was offered remarriage a few times, a testament to my reputation as a valued wife. But each time I said no. I wanted to focus all my attention on my children and ensuring their success. Luckily, I made sure that the new ruling khan, Ogedai, was a friend of mine. He put me in charge of the land my husband once ruled, meaning I was now in charge of Eastern Mongolia, parts of Iran and North China. I also negotiated being given part of Hebei province after it was conquered in 1236! Vast areas of the lands I once only heard tales of were now under my control, and all because of my great negotiation skills and intelligence.

My political skills did not go unnoticed. Ogedai had heard of my knowledge and would often come to me for advice, just as my late husband had. I'll admit that sometimes when he was talking me through a particularly tricky problem, I would imagine it was Tolui speaking, back in the yurt we shared together as husband and wife. But I had to focus on the future – my sons' futures. Ogedai put me in charge of the empire's administration, meaning I helped to secure the lands captured by Genghis Khan. I was helping to keep our empire running. I had to, until my sons could take over for me.

As my responsibilities grew, word travelled among our people of my skill. When a representative of the Pope once visited Mongolia in 1246, he wrote of me, **'Among the Mongols this lady is most renowned.'** But despite all my personal achievements, everything I did was to ensure the success of my sons. Their future was where my ambitions lay.

But ambition can be dangerous when it goes too far. The ruling khan after Ogedai was not so keen on me and several other powerful women in government. Guyuk tried to take away our power, and without my influence in government my children would never have risen to become khans! So, I did what I had to do… When he set off for a campaign in the Middle East, Guyuk died under suspicious circumstances.

Although I have told you much, I will keep the whole truth to that story buried deep under the desert sands.

LEGACY

We have come to the last phase of my life. In 1252, at sixty-two, I fell ill, and it is there that my story on Earth ends.

But as for my legacy and my goal to make sure my sons went on to be great leaders – well…

My first boy, Mongke, went on to be Great Khan of the Mongol Empire. I saw him rule for just a few short months before I passed away.

After him, Kublai went on to be Great Khan of the Mongol Empire and Yuan Dynasty.

Then Hulagu went on to be Great Khan of the Ilkhanate dynasty that ruled

Persia, Turkey, Georgia and Armenia.

Ariq also went on to be Great Khan, though only for a short time, in 1260.

I watched them all from afar, all their successes and their time in power. And I knew that it was my ambition and political influence that put them there. Being the mother of four great Mongol khans means that our legacies are intertwined.

In 1335, eighty-three years after my death, I was enshrined in a Christian church in Guangzhou. And so I live on in my final identity as a Nestorian saint. You can visit a shrine to me and my husband in the Eastern Palace of Genghis Khan's Mausoleum in Inner Mongolia today. It is humbling to know I haven't been forgotten.

This is the end of my story – long and winding as the Silk Road. But if you remember only some of it, let it be this: Sorghaghtani Beki was princess, advisor, mother of four khans and saint in the late, great Mongol Empire.

GLOSSARY

Alliance – a group of people, countries or groups that share goals and agree to work together

Chieftain – a leader of a clan or people

Concubine – a woman who lives with a man but is not married to him

Khan – a title given to rulers in central Asia, Afghanistan and some other Muslim countries

Mausoleum – an impressive building housing a tomb

Silk Road – an ancient trade route linking central China with the eastern Mediterranean

Steppe – a large, dry grass plain

ILLUSTRATED BY JEN KHATUN

RABBAN BAR SAUMA

BY BALI RAI

Many people know of Marco Polo – the Italian merchant who visited China in the late thirteenth century. But have you ever heard of Rabban Bar Sauma? He travelled from China to Europe, reaching as far west as France. He did this around the same time as Marco Polo. Only, most people have never heard his story. Rabban Bar Sauma is often called the **'reverse Marco Polo'**. His tale is every bit as exciting, interesting and important.

Rabban Bar Sauma was born in 1230, in Zhongdu, China. He was an Onggud Turk. His tribal lands were in North China, and had been conquered by the Mongols. Rabban was a Nestorian Christian. The Nestorians were the most eastern of all Christians at the time, and had their own church and their own leaders. Rabban's parents valued education, so he was well-read and spoke three languages: Syriac, Turkic and Chinese.

By the age of twenty, Rabban decided to become a priest in the Nestorian Church. His parents were very proud and began to search for a woman for

Rabban to marry. Arranged marriages were normal in those times, and parents decided who their children would marry. However, Rabban did not wish to marry anyone. At twenty-five years of age, he took monastic vows and became a monk. His parents were horrified, as they had already found him a suitable bride.

Rabban moved to an isolated region, where he built himself a cell. He entered his new home and lived a simple, solitary life as a monk. He wished to meditate and pray, and did so for a long time. Some years later, a young man called Markos found him. Markos had travelled for fifteen days to find Rabban's retreat. He wished to learn from the priest, and to stay with him and study. Rabban accepted, and Markos become his pupil. Very little is known about how they lived, but it would have been a very simple existence. That would change, however.

In 1275, Rabban decided to go on a pilgrimage. Nestorian Christians had many sacred sites and shrines, and Rabban wanted to see them. His biggest wish was to visit Jerusalem. Markos agreed to go along. Many local people warned against the journey. The route was long and challenging, and would be dangerous. Rabban and Markos did not listen. They knew that they would face a difficult trip, but they were determined to go. With an entourage of camel handlers, interpreters, cooks and guards, they set off from Zhongdu to Ningxia province.

From North-east China, they followed the edge of the Taklamakan Desert. The vast Taklamakan was regularly battered by sandstorms, and the world's second-largest shifting-sand desert. Most people who entered the desert did not survive its harsh conditions. They travelled for 800 kilometres, until they arrived at the oasis of Khotan. They had only found fresh water eight times in two months. They must have been tired and thirsty, short of supplies and ready for a rest. However, they were stuck in Khotan for six months, avoiding a war between Kublai Khan of the Mongols and the state of Mien. They only moved on once the war had ended.

Their next stop was another oasis town, Kashgar, and from there they travelled to Tus, in modern-day Iran. Tus was home to a Nestorian monastery known as Mar Sehyon. It is believed that they reached the site in 1279, almost four years after setting off. After a short stay in Tus, they went on to Baghdad, in modern-day Iraq. Baghdad was a legendary walled city – once called the **'Round City'**. It had been important for many years and was a centre for learning and trade. By the time Rabban and Markos arrived, Mongol raiders had destroyed many of Baghdad's wonders, but it remained an important part of Rabban's pilgrimage. Baghdad was home to the Catholicos, the head of the Nestorian Church. South of the city were the holy sites, including the supposed tomb of the prophet Ezekiel in Mosul. Once again, bad luck and war prevented further travel. They were stuck in Baghdad. While there, Rabban gained the trust of the Mongol ruler of Persia, the Ilkhan.

Eventually, the Ilkhan asked Rabban to journey west on a special mission. Rabban was elderly by then and travelled alone. Markos had become the new Catholicos of the Nestorian Church and remained in Baghdad. The Ilkhan gave Rabban gold and animals, and a team of helpers, and they left for Constantinople via the Black Sea. The Byzantine city was surrounded by huge walls and must have seemed very impressive. Constantinople was one of the most important cities in the medieval world, and the site of many wars. When Rabban arrived by ship, the emperor Andronicus II gave him a house to stay in.

While there Rabban toured the city's many holy sites. He saw the great church of Hagia Sophia, the Church of Holy Wisdom (the modern-day Aya

Sofya mosque), with its spectacular dome. He saw many sacred Christian relics, such as the hand of John the Baptist, a picture of the Virgin Mary and the bowl in which Jesus was said to have turned water into wine. There were also tombs to the great emperors Constantine and Justinian. For a devout Christian, Constantinople was a very important city indeed. Rabban must have been delighted to finally visit.

His time in Constantinople was short. Within weeks, he set sail again, crossing the Aegean Sea past Greece to Italy. He was greeted by King Charles II of Naples, but yet again, he arrived in the midst of war. This time he witnessed a great naval battle between Naples and Aragon, in which it is said that 12,000 men died. And Mount Etna, in the nearby Kingdom of Sicily, erupted in the midst of fighting. Rabban watched from the roof of a mansion as huge galleys crashed into each other out at sea.

After Naples, Rabban went north to the great city of Rome. He had hoped to meet Pope Honorius, but arrived too late. Honorius had died, and the cardinals of the Vatican were busy electing a new pope. Nevertheless, they were fascinated by Rabban. Here was a member of the Nestorian Church – the Church of the East, as they called it – and they had lots of questions. Rabban was also taken to many sacred sites and churches, including the Church of St John the Baptist, where a cloak said to have belonged to Jesus was kept.

From Rome, Rabban went to Tuscany and Genoa, stopping at many more sacred sites. Then he travelled to France and made his way to Paris. King Phillipe IV sent a company of knights to escort Rabban into the city – a great honour. Later, Rabban explained his secret mission from the Ilkhan of Persia. The Persians wanted allies with whom they could retake Jerusalem from the Mamluks who had conquered it. News soon reached Rabban that King Edward II of England was in Bordeaux (which was held by the English at that time). Hastily, Rabban set off to meet Edward II and gain his support in Persia. The English king gave Rabban money and promised an alliance – one that never came into existence.

Satisfied, Rabban and his entourage returned to Italy and spent the winter in Genoa. There was a new pope in Rome, Nicholas IV, and Rabban was finally able to meet him a few months later. It was Holy Week (the week before Easter) and Rome was full of pilgrims, processions and ceremonies. Rabban gave the Pope a letter from the Ilkhan, and gifts too. But when Rabban asked the Pope for holy relics to take back to the East, the Pope was unsure. In the end, he gave Rabban a piece of the Virgin Mary's cape. He also gave a jewelled crown for Markos, the Catholicos and Rabban's former pupil. The Pope made Rabban his emissary in the East, another great honour.

After many more months of travel, Rabban finally returned to Baghdad. Heading into old age, he was suffering from his arduous journey. He asked the Ilkhan for permission to retire. With his wish granted, Rabban went to Maragah (modern-day Iran) and built a church. Rabban died very soon after completing it, in 1294.

His travels made him a significant figure from the Middle Ages. Rabban was the first Eastern traveller to visit medieval Europe. He also met three kings, an emperor and a pope. He brought the Nestorian Church to Rome, and exchanged gifts and letters that forged a link between the East and the West. His journey may have been the opposite of Marco Polo, but Rabban Bar Sauma was just as important. His name and his achievements deserve to be remembered.

GLOSSARY

Cell – a prison-style, locked room

Kublai Khan – grandson of the great Mongol ruler, Genghis Khan, and the first Mongol ruler of China. He founded the Yuan Dynasty in the thirteenth century.

Mamluks – former slave soldiers who became a powerful political force. They ruled Egypt and Syria from 1250 to 1517.

Middle Ages – also known as the medieval age. This started when the Roman Empire collapsed in AD500 and lasted until around 1500.

Monastic vows – promises to follow religious rules, in service to God. They exist in many religions.

Relic – an ancient object that has religious significance or historical importance

Zhongdu – the capital of the Jin Dynasty in medieval China. Now part of Beijing's southwestern Xicheng district.

ILLUSTRATED BY HANNAH LI

KING SEJONG

BY CYNTHIA SO

King Sejong faced a conundrum.

He had solved many puzzles before. He had devoted his reign to coming up with solutions and assembled a whole team of scholars who could help him out. He called them his Hall of Worthies – a group of dedicated young people whose brains buzzed with ideas and whose natural habitat was the library, where they could learn all there was to know about every subject under the sun.

He had stocked that library full of books from China, so that they could find lessons that would be useful in Korea. They would read everything they could get their hands on, and they would go out and talk to the people of the nation and ask them questions, and they would come back with maps and measurements, samples and sketches. Their research led to innovations in medicine, music and mathematics – new instruments, new cures, new calendars.

But there was one problem he didn't trust them with.

He summoned his favourite scientist, Jang Yeong-sil, to his side. Together they stood at the magnificent water clock Jang had designed. It was not the only thing that had been born from Jang's clever mind. He had invented sundials so people throughout the country could tell the time. Water clocks served the same purpose, but they were much more expensive to make, and sundials made it possible to bring time to everyone.

'Jang,' said the king, 'do you remember when you first came here to the palace to work for me?'

Jang nodded. 'I was honoured that you recognized my engineering skills, Your Majesty, despite my humble origins.'

'But others were not so happy,' the king replied.

Jang's face darkened. 'Well, some nobles could not bear the thought of a mere peasant rising to the same ranks as them.'

'You are worth ten of those men,' the king muttered.

Jang's expression lit up with a smile. 'Did you call me here just to reminisce, Your Majesty, or was there business to discuss?'

'I am at a loss,' the king admitted. 'There is something that has been troubling me, and I do not know what to do about it.'

'What is the matter?'

King Sejong closed his eyes. His vision had been steadily worsening over the past few years, and it was painful and tiring to keep his eyes open sometimes. Instead he focused on the burbling noise of the water flowing through the pipes of the clock in front of him, while he gathered his thoughts. **'The issue,'** he said, finally, **'is that most of my people cannot read or write.'**

'Chinese characters are quite complicated…' Jang acknowledged.

'They are. But we do not speak Chinese. We speak Korean.'

A long, long time ago, their ancestors had adopted Chinese characters to write down their spoken language of Korean, so they could communicate with people from China and study Chinese texts. But it was difficult to capture the pronunciation of words in one language using the script of another. And there were many Chinese characters – tens of thousands of them. To learn all of them required too much time and effort, which most common people could not afford to spend.

'That is true,' Jang said. **'So why are you not presenting this problem to the Hall of Worthies? Why are we having this conversation in private? I'm sure they would jump at the chance to tackle this issue for you.'**

'Would they, though?' the king said, frowning. **'Think of how many of them turned their noses up at you, until I berated them.'**

'Yes, but they have done great things to help the peasantry before. All of us worked long and hard on that agricultural project to make lives easier for farmers.'

They had indeed. They had trekked throughout the land to visit farms everywhere, so they could see what tools were being used, how crops were being watered and so on. They even studied dirt! His prim and proper scholars stuck their hands into mud all over the country and figured out how to classify soil into different grades according to how well plants could grow in it. Jang also did his bit, devising new rain gauges to measure rainfall. The result of their work? More plentiful harvests and fewer people who had to go hungry.

King Sejong was proud of them. But this was different.

'They are willing to help farmers be farmers, of course,' he said. **'But I do not believe all of them would be willing to help farmers become scholars, like you. That is how they will see it. They will think that we are creating more opportunities for peasants to transform into nobles, and they will not like that one whit.'**

'You may be right.' Jang sighed. **'But you are a wonderful scholar and linguist yourself. You are a wise and intelligent king. Perhaps this is something you do not need to rely on the Hall of Worthies for.'**

'Perhaps,' said the king, stroking his long beard pensively. He could do it. He was fascinated by the way languages worked, and he had always been studious. When he was little he never thought the burden of rulership would be his. His older brother Yangnyeong had been next in line to inherit the throne. He thought he would be free to live a leisurely life, whiling away his time with his nose deep in some book or other. But when he was just twenty-one, his father suddenly named him the heir to the throne instead of Yangnyeong, and left him to become king just a few short months later.

While he had never thought the job would fall to him, he was determined to do the best he could. He wanted nothing more than for his people to prosper. And he knew that this was something he could do, and it would help his people. He was convinced of it.

But his eyes… He rubbed at them. They were not what they used to be. Reading was difficult these days. Words blurred and swam.

Still, he had to try.

'Thank you, Jang,' he said, and he retired to his room to begin his great work.

*

Several years later, sitting upon his throne, King Sejong announced that he had created a Korean alphabet, called Hangul. He had thought long and hard about what would make it easiest for everyone to learn. It consisted of only twenty-eight characters, and he had developed it with Korean sounds in mind. The shape of each letter mirrored the movements of the mouth and tongue when forming those sounds.

Hangul made it for his country, for his people. It was the product of his love for them. Whenever his eyes hurt, working late into the night, he would remind himself of his goal – everybody in the kingdom being able to read and write – and he would persevere.

He had recently been to the hot springs in Icheon, famed for their healing properties, but they had not miraculously returned his full sight to him. No matter – he had completed the alphabet, at last.

His officials were surprised. Some of them, predictably, were angry.

Choe Manri, one of the scholars from the Hall of Worthies, was one of them. The look of utter alarm on his face was almost comical. **'Y-your Majesty!'** he spluttered, cheeks red and eyes wide. **'This is… uh… an admirable project indeed, and it is proof of your powerful intellect.'** His expression indicated he was of the opposite opinion. **'But we must urge you to reconsider.'** Ah, there it was. **'The use of Chinese characters is a mark of our sophisticated culture and an important part of our relationship with China! The introduction of this Korean alphabet will upset the social order; if every peasant learns to read and write, then this country will be thrown into chaos. Why waste your precious time on trivial things like this when there are many more urgent issues of greater significance for our kingdom that deserve your attention?'**

King Sejong met Jang Yeong-sil's eyes across the room. Had he not been afraid that this would happen? But the alphabet existed now. There was no taking it back.

'Choe,' the king said, in what he hoped was a reasonable tone. **'I hear and understand your concerns, but the literacy of my people is something dear to my heart, and I will not be swayed from this path. I will not rest until we've spread the alphabet far and wide.'**

He gave orders for books to be printed about the new alphabet, ignoring the protests of Choe and other noble officials like Choe, who felt that their positions would be threatened if more peasants became educated. After he had dismissed them, he closed his eyes.

'Congratulations, Your Majesty.' Jang's voice interrupted his thoughts.

'You did it.'

King Sejong smiled. He had.

Six hundred years later, the alphabet that he invented is still used in Korea. Hangul is now the official writing system used by every Korean, even though several kings after Sejong opposed its use – one even banned it. King Sejong is a celebrated hero, his face printed on stamps and banknotes. He is remembered as King Sejong the Great, a man who never stopped in pursuit of his dream of making education more accessible for all.

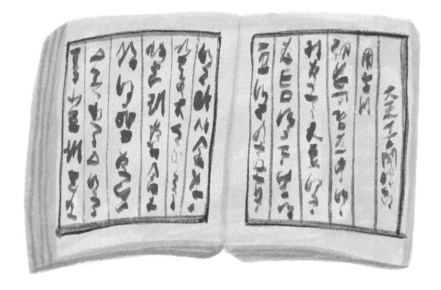

GLOSSARY

Scholar – a person who has much knowledge, usually gained from research and study

ILLUSTRATED BY JOCELYN KAO

MATSUO BASHŌ

BY CYNTHIA SO

A crackling sound. The smell of burning in his nostrils.

His hut was on fire!

Matsuo Bashō leaped out of his bed. Fires were not uncommon in the city where he lived – then called Edo, nowadays called Tokyo – but that didn't make it any less terrifying to be in the middle of one. His heart pounded. He ran out of his cottage through the thick grey haze, coughing. Everything around him was ablaze. Close by, orange and red flames raced up the trunk of his beloved banana tree, but he did not stop to mourn it. His legs kept pumping, carrying him towards the river. The water was shallow enough for him to wade through, but it was shockingly cold.

When he reached the other side, he climbed onto the muddy bank and took a moment to breathe. His clothes dripped. Shivering, he looked back at the columns of smoke rising into the sky, ruined wooden buildings lit by ravenous fire.

He was not one to be attached to material things, but even so he was heartbroken to lose his little home, and more than that, his beautiful banana tree. He had sat under its enormous leaves many a day, writing his poems and watching the world around him. One of his students had planted it beside his hut as a gift. It was the very reason he was called **'Bashō'** – the Japanese word for banana plant. His birth name was Matsuo Kinsaku but he had loved 'bashō' so much he adopted it as his pen name. He had admired how it stood up against the wind and the rain. Fierce gales had not blown it down. And now it was gone.

He remembered being a child again. His family were descended from samurai, brave and strong warriors, and they had high hopes that he would become one too. But when he was a boy, he was sent to work as a servant to Todo Yoshitada, and it changed his life. At first, he hadn't been too excited about the prospect of serving the local lord's young son, but Yoshitada was only a couple years older than him, and he found out that Yoshitada was interested in poetry too. He ended up spending more time with Yoshitada composing short, pithy poems called haikus than doing the job he was supposed to do.

Yoshitada became his friend. Yoshitada understood him. And Yoshitada died, suddenly, at the age of twenty-four.

It was like a fire, destroying everything he had known.

Matsuo, who had not yet adopted the name Bashō, decided then that he could not fulfil his family's dreams of him becoming a samurai. They were not *his* dreams. He knew what he truly loved: poetry. Even though poetry wasn't considered a serious career option at the time, he wanted to try his best to pursue it.

When he first moved to Edo, he didn't have much. He had published some haikus, but it was once in the capital that he really started to make a living as a poet. He participated in contests – once with sixty other poets! – and students began to flock to him to learn poetry. He grew in fame. People read and respected his work.

And now, drenched in river water, his throat still raw with smoke, he felt as though he had nothing again. No home, no banana tree. Bashō was without his dear bashō, his namesake.

But he was unharmed. He was alive.

He stood up. He thought about what inspired his poetry. Often he would complain about life in the city, although it was seen as the place to be. All the noble lords and samurai lived there, and they supported poor artists with their wealth. Bashō wished it wasn't the case. Edo was so … busy. There were always a million things demanding his attention. He yearned for the countryside, for nature. For undisturbed woods and still lakes. Wind rustling through leaves and the twittering of birds.

It wasn't as if he couldn't connect to nature in Edo. There were cherry blossoms in the spring and fireflies in the summer. Leaves turning gold in the autumn and flurries of soft, white snow in the winter. But there were people, people everywhere!

It was why he loved his small hut and his banana tree, in a quieter neighbourhood. In the theatre district where he had lived for years previously, puppet shows and all sorts of other performances attracted rowdy crowds every night, and the lanterns were aglow from dusk till dawn.

But in his secluded banana tree hut, he could be away from the bustle of the city. He cared about his students and he liked teaching them, but even they got too loud for him sometimes, and he would lock his gate to keep everybody away, just so he could think and write.

Perhaps this disaster was a sign that he should leave Edo for the countryside, where there were fewer people and fewer fires. He would have his poetry, and that would be enough.

So he left. He stayed in a sleepy mountain village for a while, but his pupils begged him to return. **'We'll build another cottage for you,'** they promised. **'And we'll plant another banana tree.'**

And they did.

Bashō could not resist. He came back. But not long after that, his mother passed away. He was overwhelmed with sadness.

He felt like the banana tree, battered by a storm, leaves torn and ragged. He left the city again, and this time he went wandering.

He walked and walked. On foot, he experienced swathes of Japan. His heart lightened at the sights he saw: the rolling fields, the vast sky.

Travel wasn't easy at the time. In fact, it could be very dangerous, and his friends were afraid that he would meet an unlucky end – at the hands of murderous bandits perhaps, or from one of those illnesses he was prone to, or simply from a lack of food and shelter out there in the wilderness. But Bashō was undeterred. He was determined to enjoy nature as purely as possible. He dressed himself up as a monk in plain robes to seem penniless and make himself an unappealing target. The perils of the countryside were nothing compared to fires in Edo, he thought!

Thankfully, he managed to stay safe, and he had a wonderful time. He spoke to humble farmers. He visited other poets and people who were great fans of his poetry. As he roamed, he wrote diaries and lots and lots of poems, creating a whole new literary form that combined prose and haikus to describe his journeys. Living the simple life, he felt at peace and so much closer to nature – to the source of his inspiration. After all, the haiku was also a simple art form. A haiku was made up of just three lines. Three lines were all he needed. Without distractions, he could concentrate on what was important: the beauty in everything around him.

The stars twinkled; the crows cawed; the cicadas sang; the rain pattered.

But no matter how far he travelled, a part of him missed Edo.

It wasn't the city he missed. He did think about his students and his friends, but it was the banana tree hut that he longed for most of all. It was modest, but it was the tiny corner of Earth that he called home. At night, he would worry about his banana plant, and hope that it was still thriving.

So eventually he returned to Edo, and there it was: his lovely banana tree, swaying gently in the breeze.

Home.

Back in the city, he continued to write. One of his most famous poems, **'The Frog'**, was written then:

> **An ancient pond**
> **A frog jumps in**
> **The sound of water**

The poets of Edo even gathered at the banana tree hut a few months later for a contest on the subject of frogs! That was how much they adored his poem. Nobody captured nature like he did.

Bashō never stopped travelling – his most famous travel narrative records the time he spent five months walking with his disciple Sora, covering nearly two thousand kilometres – but he always came home to his banana tree. He wrote several haikus and an entire essay about it. Even after the second one died, his friends planted a third for him. As a person who was often ill, he was cheered by the sight of the plant, its broad leaves easily ripped by strong gusts. It was his companion in life – just as frail as him, but resilient too.

Today, thanks to Bashō's poems, which are loved by many around the world, the haiku is still a popular form of poetry within Japan and outside it. If you ever come across a banana tree, why not try sitting under it, closing your eyes and writing a haiku in Bashō's honour? Just three lines and a love for nature: that's all you need.

GLOSSARY

Cicada – a large insect with two pairs of thin, clear wings. The male cicada makes a loud, shrill noise.

Haiku – a Japanese poem of three lines. The first line has five syllables, the second line has seven syllables and the third line has five syllables.

Namesake – a person or thing that has the same name as another

Pen name – a name used by a writer instead of their real name

Prose – writing or speech in its ordinary form of a series of sentences

Swathe – a broad area of something

ILLUSTRATED BY AMANDA YOSHIDA

SAKE DEAN MAHOMET

BY BALI RAI

Have you ever spent an evening tucking into a delicious takeaway curry, just out of a fragrant bubble bath, with freshly washed hair? It's a warm and cosy feeling, isn't it? Well, you and I have one person to thank for that. His name was Sake Dean Mahomet and he introduced Britain to both shampoo and curry. His story is a tale of rags to riches, and back again.

Sake Dean Mahomet was born in 1759, in Patna, northern India. As a child he watched the British take control of India. Eventually, the British ruled the entire country, and people like Dean became British subjects. Many Indians tried to resist British control. They did not want to be ruled by outsiders. Some, like Dean's father and elder brother, worked with the newcomers. Dean's family were poor. They had no choice but to work for their new rulers.

At the age of eleven, Dean also left home to work for the British. He became a servant to the East India Company Army. One of the officers,

Captain Godfrey Baker, took great interest in Dean and encouraged him. With this support, Dean soon rose through the ranks, to become a subedar, or lieutenant. Dean then began to train as a surgeon.

He moved around India with the army, learning new skills and gaining experience. He marched through jungles, and across hills and plains, and visited places across the subcontinent, including Dhaka, Delhi and Madras (which is now called Chennai). The distances he travelled were huge. Delhi to Madras alone is over two thousand kilometres! What an experience that must have been for a poor young man.

However, Dean wasn't always popular with other Indians. Many of them disliked anyone who worked for the British. He was attacked a few times as he travelled the countryside with his comrades. And, even though Captain Baker supported and liked Dean, Indians were not treated as well as British troops were. Dean would have been kept separate from the officers at camp and when eating. So, despite his early adventures, his life wasn't always easy.

Then, in 1783, Captain Baker was caught up in a huge scandal. He had to resign from the army and decided to return to his home in Ireland. Dean made a decision that would change his life forever. Instead of staying in India, Dean chose to join Captain Baker – who he would later describe as his best friend – on his journey west. They travelled on a ship called the *Christianburg*. The journey took several months and Dean must have been both excited and terrified. Any earlier voyages he'd taken around the coast of India had been short. This was a very long passage, to a country he didn't know.

Eventually, Dean settled in Cork, in Ireland. While there, Dean attended a local school to improve his English. Soon, he fell in love with a local woman,

Janet Daley. They wanted to get married, but faced problems. Her family did not approve of Dean, but not because he was Indian. Janet's family were Protestant Christians, and they thought Dean might be a Catholic. There was a lot of mistrust and tension between Protestants and Catholics. However, when Janet's family found out Dean was not Catholic, they allowed the marriage to go ahead.

Dean and Janet had seven children, and life must have been hectic. Still, Dean found time to write a book about his travels. In 1794, when *The Travels of Dean Mahomet* was first published, Dean became the first Indian to publish a book in English. This was an incredible achievement. But Cork began to feel too small, and Dean had big plans. In 1807, Dean, Janet and their children left Ireland and moved to London. Their first address was 7 Little Ryder Street.

In London, Dean started working for a Scottish nobleman. He was called Basil Cochrane and had also lived in British India. His company supplied the Royal Navy and made him a fortune. In London, with Dean's help, Basil Cochrane set up a vapour bath house. These were steam baths that both Basil Cochrane and Dean believed would help people feel healthier. Their customers also received massages, which gave Dean a brilliant idea. He began to add Indian herbs to massage oil, and he called the resulting mixture 'shampoo'. These **'shampooing'** massages became very popular. Dean didn't realize it at the time, but he had created something that would outlive him.

However, Dean quickly grew tired of the vapour baths. In 1809, he and Janet opened the Hindoostane Coffee House on George Street in Marylebone. It was London's first ever Indian restaurant. Dean and Janet sold curry and other dishes to local people. Many of their customers had lived in India.

They also sold coffee, which was becoming very popular at the time. The restaurant was unique and must have caused quite a stir with the public.

Dean and Janet worked very hard, but the restaurant was not a success. They struggled to pay their bills and to attract enough customers. Rich people didn't eat in restaurants in those days; they preferred to eat at home. Those who wanted curry and other British Indian dishes would simply hire Indian chefs. When it became too expensive to continue, Dean and Janet closed down their business. They left London shortly after and moved to Brighton. Again, they didn't realize what they had achieved. Dean and Janet had introduced curry to Britain. Today, curry houses are a much-loved part of British culture.

Brighton was very popular in 1812. Many of London's richest people spent their summer by the south coast. London was dirty and crowded, while Brighton had clean streets, fresh air and the sea. There were brand-new houses and buildings, and green parks and squares. It was a very fashionable place to be. However, Dean did not have a job and he needed to earn some money. Then he had another great idea. People visited the seaside for health reasons. The fresh breeze and sunshine made them feel better. Dean already had a reputation for his shampoo. Surely, he could start again in Brighton?

Dean began giving massages again, and his business quickly grew. Soon he opened another steam room and once more offered shampooing. His special blends of Indian herbs and oils proved popular. After meeting some people who knew King George IV, Dean offered his services. The king enjoyed the treatment, and so did his successor King William IV. Dean soon earned a Royal Warrant of Appointment, and became the **'shampooing surgeon'** to the king.

However, despite clever advertising, Dean's business eventually began to fail. He even wrote another book about Indian and British medicine, but it didn't help. Shampooing became less fashionable, and as his work dried up, his debts grew larger. Soon, Dean was poor again, and he died in 1851. Nevertheless, he had left his mark. He created a legacy that still exists today. Sake Dean Mahomet brought curry and shampoo to the British, became the first Indian to publish a book in English, and was shampooing surgeon to the king. **Not bad for a poor boy from Patna!**

GLOSSARY

British India – the areas of South Asia under British rule from 1858 to 1947. Also called the British Raj.

Curry house – a restaurant that serves Indian food

East India Company Army – the private army of the East India Company (EIC). The EIC was founded in 1600 and formed to trade in the Indian Ocean region.

ILLUSTRATED BY AALIYA JALEEL

NIIJIMA YAE

BY REKHA WAHEED

THE GREAT FEMALE SAMURAI

Many years ago, a girl by the name of Yaeko was born into the respected Yamamoto family in Japan. They lived in the remote valley of Aizu, which was famous for its samurai warriors, cherry blossom trees and towering Tsuruga Castle. Yae, as she liked to be called, was a descendant of the powerful samurai Yamamoto Kansuke. Her father, Gonpachi, was a samurai and a highly ranked gun official. Kakuma and Saburo, her brothers, were also accomplished samurai. With a family of weaponry and military experts, it was no surprise that little Yae yearned to become a warrior.

From a very young age, Yae watched young warriors rush into the Nisshinkan. This was a special school just for the children of samurai. It is here that they trained to become fearless fighters skilled in archery, spearmanship, swordsmanship and horsemanship.

However, in the 1800s, few samurai girls learned combat skills. They were largely expected to learn sewing and homemaking. But Yae had warrior blood running through her veins, and this was not the life she wanted.

'Courage, loyalty, integrity, sincerity, respect, compassion and honour! I know the Way of the Warrior! Show me how to shoot, not sew!' Yae pleaded.

YU: COURAGE
Heroic courage is intelligent and strong

Gonpachi paid no attention to his little daughter. Yae hounded Kakuma, who was a teacher at the Nisshinkan, but her older brother also refused to listen. Strong and spirited, Yae was not to be silenced. She pleaded and persisted, implored and entreated, and persevered and persuaded until Gonpachi finally relented. Admiring her determination, Kakuma taught Yae how to handle weapons in the firing range within the samurai residence.

The townspeople of Aizu were outraged! It was unheard of for a young girl to train in gunmanship, especially when few Japanese people knew how to use a gun.

Finding courage in her samurai spirit, Yae spent all her childhood learning how to shoot. Weeks, months and seasons slipped by. Yae, now a teenager, became a brilliant markswoman.

'Only for the courageous,' Kakuma said, gifting Yae with a rare Spencer rifle. Yae threw her arms around her brother's neck. The rifle was more than a precious gift. It was acknowledgement that she had courage, and courage was one of the ways of the samurai.

Yae went further. She secretly read her father's gunnery books. She learned about cannons and rifles, and how to deploy troops. She soaked up information about new Western technology by listening in on discussions Kakuma had with his peers. This is how she met Shonosuke Kawasaki, a samurai, weapons expert and teacher at the Nisshinkan. They married when Yae turned twenty.

CHU: LOYALTY
Remain fiercely true to warriors you are responsible for

Far away from Aizu, much bigger changes were taking place in Japan. Emperor Meiji ended a 200-year rule that had kept Japan closed off from the rest of the world. He also wanted to reclaim power away from the shoguns who had ruled over Japan for many centuries. But many of these chief military commanders did not approve and they rebelled against the emperor.

War broke out between the imperial army and the shogunates in 1868. Seventeen major battles defined the Boshin War, and one of the last battles took place in Aizu. News travelled fast, and samurai families sought protection within Tsuruga Castle. The shogun-loyal samurai were fearless warriors and stood ready, armed with rifles and muskets, and katana swords and yari spears.

Emperor Meiji's formidable forces advanced. Their feet thundered on the valley's cold, hard ground until troops armed with modern rifles and mighty cannons surrounded Tsuruga Castle.

'Fire!' the commanders bellowed. The imperial army bombarded the castle with cannonballs and the booming explosions made Aizu quake. Bullets showered over the castle like rain, and a blizzard of arrows and spears shrilled through the sky. The battle was bloody and brutal.

'The interesting thing about guns is that they make women as strong as men,' Yae said, grabbing her Spencer rifle when she discovered that Saburo, her brother, had been killed at the Battle of Toba–Fushimi.

Dressed in Saburo's kimono, and with her hair cut short, Yae dodged the carving and cleaving of swords, the blitz and barrage of bullets, and the pounding and pummelling of the cannonballs to get into Tsuruga Castle. Respected as one of the few gun experts within the castle, Yae fought as one of the rifle soldiers and deployed musket-armed troops. She took part in night raids into the imperial army camps, and fought alongside Gonpachi, Kakuma and Shonosuke.

'Wet blanket!' Yae yelled, using her knowledge of weaponry to fearlessly extinguish delay-fused cannonballs.

Yae also taught women how to prepare ammunition, and joined the wives and daughters of the samurai to cook and clean, extinguish ferocious fires and tend to the wailing wounded.

Yae was a heroic, loyal samurai. It is hard to believe that she was twenty-two.

But the siege was long. It sapped the strength and spirit of the Aizu samurai. After months of bombardment, the imperial army took control of Tsuruga Castle. Yae lost her father, Gonpachi, during the battle. Shonosuke was captured as a prisoner of war along with Kakuma, who had lost his sight.

Devastated by the defeat, a weeping Yae used her hairpin to carve a poem into the white mortar wall of Tsuruga Castle:

Tomorrow night,
Who, from I know not where,
Will gaze upon it here,
My dear castle drenched in moonlight.

Yae found shelter in a neighbouring town and remained separated from her husband until they divorced in 1871. She was often treated harshly for rebelling against the emperor. Life as a defeated Aizu samurai was not easy.

GI: INTEGRITY
Warriors make full commitment to their decisions

As cherry blossoms flower every spring, the warrior in Yae found a new passion in education. Yae learned English quickly after moving to Kyoto to live with Kakuma, who had become a prominent statesman. She became a secondary school teacher for girls and helped write one of Kyoto's first English language guidebooks in 1873. During this period, Yae became a Christian and she met an American-educated Protestant missionary called Joseph Hardy Neesima (Niijima Jo in Japanese).

'She is always doing something outrageous!' Kakuma said to Jo, who was looking for a non-traditional Japanese wife. Yae and Jo married in 1876, and it was the first Protestant wedding in Kyoto.

Yae became Niijima Yae. But she was no submissive Japanese wife! Yae called Jo by his first name, walked ahead of him and gave him advice on important matters. It was scandalous!

'There's the bad wife!' the shocked local community shouted at Yae. This was never going to faze a true daughter of Aizu! Yae continued to defy

Japanese society's expectations of women. She sat next to her husband when travelling in rickshaws. She wore kimonos with shoes and Western hats, and she even dared to wear rare and expensive Western dresses.

But commitment to her ideals of equality came with a cost. The tradition-loving men and women of Kyoto disapproved of Yae's daring ways, religious beliefs and unconventional marriage. She was soon let go from her teaching role.

MAKATO: SINCERITY
Speaking and doing are the same action

With a mind as sharp as a samurai's sword, Yae channelled her energies into helping Jo open a school, now known as Doshisha University.

'A just society needs modernized, educated Japanese women,' Yae said, opening the Doshisha School for Girls in 1877. It was the first in Japan to provide Western-style education to girls, and she taught there for thirteen years.

Throughout this period, Yae advocated for the samurai, cared for them and employed them in her school. Unafraid of speaking at local meetings, Yae even spoke on their behalf. This is something Japanese women did not do!

'She is afraid of no one when she is convinced of her duty,' Jo said, greatly admiring his wife's bold and independent traits.

Yae had spent her life standing up to many people, including her father, soldiers and even the governors of Kyoto. Once she was convinced that change was needed, Yae pursued it without fear.

REI: RESPECT
The true strength of a warrior becomes apparent during difficult times

Sadly, Jo passed away suddenly in 1890. As well as losing her companion and champion, the unrelenting criticisms continued. Pro-emperor students condemned her for her role in the Boshin War. Traditional community members criticized her for her bold ways, beliefs and high profile. Without Jo by her side, Yae became disheartened with the difficulties she faced. Respectfully, she stepped down from her role at Doshisha University.

'Every difficulty brings a new dawn,' Yae thought.

As a widow, Yae pursued new challenges. Having studied the highly respected samurai art of the Japanese tea ceremony and flower arrangement, she became a master of the Urasenke tea ceremony tradition in 1894. She also became a master of the Ikenobo flower ceremony. With the strength of a warrior, Yae started tea ceremony classes for women in Kyoto, and by doing so, continued to bring about change for Japanese women.

JIN: COMPASSION

Warriors develop a power that must be used for good and help at every opportunity

In 1894, Japan and China went to war and Yae volunteered as a military nurse with the Japanese Red Cross.

'A warrior knows when to use their compassion,' Yae decided.

Familiar with the conditions of war, she showed great care while treating the wounded soldiers in Hiroshima. She also trained a team of forty female nurses.

Following the war, Yae worked hard to improve the status of female nurses in Japan. Once regarded as unskilled labourers, Yae ensured that nurses were paid and respected as trained professionals. Yae's efforts were recognized by the Japanese government, and she was awarded the Order of the Sacred Crown. This was a rare honour for women in Japan.

Less than a decade later, Yae rejoined the army for the Russo-Japanese War in 1904. Once again, she used her knowledge and skills for good by serving as a nurse at the Imperial Japanese Army hospital in Osaka. For this service, Yae received her second Order of the Sacred Crown. Yae's compassionate contribution to Japan was honoured in full when she was awarded the Silver Cup at the inauguration of Emperor Showa in 1928.

MEIYO: HONOUR
Warriors have one judge of honour and character: themselves

Yae was born in the land of the samurai, and she served as a courageous warrior, distinguished educator, accomplished master of tea ceremonies and a compassionate nurse. She experienced many adversities as a woman, as an Aizu samurai and as an advocate for women's education and empowerment in Japan. Yet, Yae continued to contribute to Japanese society at every opportunity until she passed away in 1932.

Today, a bronze statue of Yae stands at Tsuruga Castle in the remote, cherry blossom-filled valley of Aizu. It honours her legacy as an iconic heroine and inspires future generations of strong-willed girls and boys all around the world.

GLOSSARY

Ikenobo – the oldest and largest school of floral art in Japan

Katana – a sword with a curved, single-edged blade and a long grip to accommodate two hands

Kimono – a traditional Japanese dressing gown and the national dress of Japan

Missionary – a person who has been sent to a place, usually a foreign country, to teach a religion to the people who live there

Nisshinkan – a special school just for the children of samurais

Samurai – a member of the Japanese military caste

Shogunate – a government controlled by a shogun (military commander)

Yari – a straight-headed spear with a metal blade at its tip

Urasenke – one of the main schools of Japanese tea ceremony

ILLUSTRATED BY AMANDA YOSHIDA

MARGARET LIN XAVIER

BY SUFIYA AHMED

LEAVING HOME

The teenage girl glanced back over her shoulder at her childhood home. She was leaving to go to school in a faraway country where it was said that there were more cold months than hot ones. She shivered despite the heat of the midday sun and wondered how she would adjust to the extreme temperature nearly halfway across the world in England. Holding her chin up, she fought the urge for one final look at her family. She had said goodbye and now needed to move forward. It was what her father expected.

Her father was Celestino Maria Xavier, a representative of the Kingdom of Siam and the new ambassador to Italy. Margaret had heard that Italy had a warmer climate and wished her father would let her live there. But there was no point arguing with him. Ambassador Xavier had made up his mind. His daughter Margaret was to be educated in England.

Some of their relatives and friends thought her father was wrong for doing this. Daughters were not meant to be schooled above basic reading and writing. They were meant to marry, support their husband, have children and run a home. Ambassador Xavier did not agree. He believed Margaret was as capable as any boy and deserved to be just as highly educated. There weren't many like her father in Siam, and dare it be said that there were not many men like him in the world.

Margaret knew she was lucky to have such a father, but she still couldn't help thinking that she would miss her home and family. She wondered when she would be able to return. Perhaps she would fall in love with England and make her home there.

THE COLD PLACE

Margaret breathed in the crisp fresh air. She was taking her morning walk in the park close to her London home. She treasured this time as the quiet allowed her to clear her mind and get ready for the day ahead. It had taken a while to get used to this different climate, but she loved it now, as much as she did her friends and colleagues. She was now twenty-six years old with a degree from the London School of Medicine for Women. As a doctor, she treated women and babies, and she loved her job. Margaret's father was very proud of her.

A gentleman on the opposite path lifted his hat.

'Good morning, Dr Lin,' he greeted.

'And to you,' Margaret replied, smiling.

She continued on for a few more minutes and then turned to walk back home. A quick breakfast, and then she would make her way to work at the Royal Free Hospital. As she closed the front door, her gaze fell on the envelope placed on the table by the maid. It was a telegram. Telegrams were emergency messages that were sent from abroad.

Was there an emergency at home?

Heart racing, Margaret picked it up and tore the seal. The message was only a few words, but she collapsed onto the floor as the meaning registered in her mind. As the sobs wracked her body, she knew it was time to go home.

RETURNING HOME
'Dr Lin.'

Margaret turned around. A senior doctor who worked for the Red Cross hospital stood by the living room door of her father's house. She pressed her palms together and bowed her head slightly in a respectful Thai greeting.

'Please come in and sit.'

'I am very sorry about your father,' the doctor said, perching on the chair. 'He was a good man and very well liked. His death was a shock to us all.'

Margaret nodded. 'Thank you.'

'Will you return to England?'

Margaret shook her head. 'I have thought about it long and hard. My life is in London, but I think I can make a new one here. I think there may be a need for my medical services in my own country.'

'Indeed, your father was very proud of the fact that you are the first female doctor in Siam,' the doctor said. 'You have made history.'

'Yes, well, my father was a very forward-thinking man who saw no difference between daughters and sons,' Margaret said with a sad smile. She was going to miss him so much. He had always been her biggest supporter.

'Where would you like to work if you remain in Siam?'

Margaret looked the doctor directly in the eye. 'Perhaps I could work at the Red Cross hospital.'

'I was hoping you would say that,' the doctor replied. 'You can start whenever you are ready.'

THE HOSPITAL
'Please … help me.'

Margaret turned towards the pitiful voice of a small, young woman who was gasping for breath on the ground. Her belly carried a baby that looked far too large for her to carry.

Margaret hurried to the young woman's side.

'Dr Lin,' the front-desk nurse objected. 'This is a hospital for rich people. We don't treat the poor here.'

'She is in need of medical attention,' Margaret snapped. 'I will not let her leave without being treated.'

The other staff looked uncomfortable but did not say anything. Margaret felt the younger woman's big belly and frowned. 'This birth is not going to be easy.'

The nurse tried to object again. 'Dr Lin, you cannot...'

Margaret's head shot up. 'Prepare a room for surgery. This patient is about to have a baby. I am a doctor and I refuse to turn her away because she can't pay the fees.'

None of the nurses moved.

'Now!' Margaret shouted.

They ran to do her bidding.

Later that evening, the young woman gave birth to a beautiful baby girl. If Margaret had not done the surgery, both the mother and baby would have died. News spread everywhere that the London-trained doctor, the first woman doctor in Siam, saved the lives of a poor mother and her baby.

More and more people who couldn't afford to pay doctors' fees came to the hospital, hoping that Margaret would treat them. She refused to turn people away and tried her best to make them better.

After a while, the rich people objected. They didn't want to share the space that was meant for them. When news of this reached Margaret's ears, she turned to her sister Chan to discuss a new idea.

Chan was a pharmacist. Like Margaret, she had been educated in England.
'What if I was to start my own clinic?'

'What do you mean?' Chan blinked.

'Well, if I open my medical clinic then I can treat whoever I want,' Margaret explained. **'There are so many sick people that cannot afford to pay, and it breaks my heart to see pregnant women and babies suffer.'**

'But how can you run a clinic without getting paid?' Chan asked reasonably. **'If you always work for free, how will you make a living?'**

Margaret whirled the end of her stethoscope round and round in her hand. That was the part that stumped her. Then her hand froze in mid-air as the solution hit. She knew what she needed to do.

That very same day, she went to see the director of the Red Cross hospital and explained her plans.

'You must fund my clinic,' Margaret finished.

The director hesitated. **'Well...'**

'Your organization has been set up to treat those in need,' Margaret said firmly. 'There are many people desperate for treatment who will die a needless death if we don't help them. Let this clinic be a place of hope for them.'

The director sat back in his chair and thought about it for a good few minutes. Then, finally, he said, 'Very well, we shall fund your clinic.' Margaret sank back in her chair and released a long breath. She hadn't realized she had been holding it in while the director thought over his decision. His confirmation meant that she could now save the lives of mothers and babies.

'What will you call this clinic?'

'Unakan.'

UNAKAN

The line outside the clinic was long. The women sat on the dusty ground with their legs crossed or folded under them as they waited their turn.

Chan turned to her sister. 'It's going to be another long day.'

Margaret nodded. 'Just like yesterday and the day before that.'

'I think some of these people aren't even local,' Chan observed. 'They have arrived on animal carts or just walked for miles to be treated by the wonderful Dr Lin.'

'And to receive medicine from the wonderful pharmacist Chan.' Margaret smiled. 'I think we make quite a team.'

*

Dr Lin died at the age of thirty-four in 1932 from influenza. She is celebrated for being the first woman doctor in Siam, now named Thailand, the land of the free. Just under half of the total doctors in Thailand are women today.

GLOSSARY

Ambassador – a person sent by a country to represent them in another country

Influenza – a disease caused by a virus, with symptoms of fever, coughing and muscle pain. Also known as 'flu'.

Red Cross – a global organization that gives medical care to victims of war and natural disaster

Stethoscope – a medical instrument used for listening to someone's heart or breathing

ILLUSTRATED BY AALIYA JALEEL

SUBEDAR KHUDADAD KHAN

BY REBEKA SHAID

Have you ever asked yourself what it means to be brave?

When Khudadad Khan grew up in his sleepy village surrounded by fields, farmers and grazing cows, he never thought he would one day bump into King George V, who would hand him a special medal for bravery. As a little boy, Khudadad lived thousands of miles away from the king's fancy palace in England. His birthplace was in rural Punjab, which means **'land of five rivers'**.

It is a place that was once ruled by the British, a place where sugarcane and rice fields are scattered across the landscape and where water buffaloes plunge into swampy canals to cool off on a sweltering day. Sweet, juicy mangoes flourish on luscious land while scaly lizards crawl up and down ancient walls. When Khudadad lived in this colourful corner of the world that is now part of Pakistan and India, he could not have imagined he would leave all of this behind to fight in a terrible war. But that is exactly what happened.

119

Back then in the early twentieth century, most people in the Punjab looked after crops and animals day in and day out, no matter if the sun burned their skin or the monsoon drenched their shirts. Khudadad carefully watched the women and men in his village. They were busy milking cattle and ploughing plots, feeding the hungry mouths of their children.

An extraordinary thought popped into Khudadad's head. **'I don't want to be a farmer,'** he pondered to himself. **'I want to be a soldier.'** He was young and eager to explore life beyond his quiet village. So, when he was only eighteen years old, he made up his mind, packed his bags and joined the British Indian Army.

But weren't the British strange! They looked nothing like Khudadad, who was a Muslim and wore a turban on his head like many of his countrymen. Not only did the British speak a different language (English!) and munch odd food (mash and custard!), but they also donned funny clothes (suits and silly hats!). The truth is, they had come to India to take control of the country, and the army was one way for them to show their power.

When Khudadad embarked on his journey in the military, he did not know what to expect. He understood life as a farmer was challenging, and he quickly found that so was life in the army. In the beginning, he served in an infantry regiment, which is made up of large groups of soldiers. Everything was new and different, even his shoes! Gone were his comfy slippers. Now, Khudadad had to wear clunky boots and a uniform – not the snug cotton clothing he was used to. Officers shouted orders and he needed to obey. Every day, Khudadad worked tirelessly and followed strict rules. Before long, he learned how to handle heavy guns because weapons play an important part in every army.

Many of the men he spent countless hours of the day training with were like him. They came from similar parts of India, often from tiny farming settlements, where people were penniless and struggled to put enough food on the table. Some of these soldiers joined the army to escape a harsh life of poverty, others followed in the footsteps of their fathers or grandfathers. But wherever they came from, Khudadad and his comrades could not have known they would soon be sent abroad to battle-scarred Europe, thrown into a war that was not theirs to fight.

The year was 1914, which sounds like a long time ago, but time is funny and goes by in an instant. Can you imagine what thoughts must have spun through Khudadad's head when he first arrived in France one day in late September? The weather was cold. The soil was muddy. The landscape was flat like a pancake.

At this time of year, the leaves were losing their colour, the sky overhead was dull and grey. Nights were long, and there was a chill in the air. Khudadad was so far away from his home and family, far away from everything he had ever known. There were no mango trees or rice fields in sight, and the only other Asians he saw were his fellow soldiers. They stood out like tropical birds in a flock of brown starlings.

It must have been lonely, but Khudadad had no time to get homesick because a few weeks after he landed in Europe, he found himself in the middle of a grisly battle. Something horrible was about to happen. He felt it, like the wind lashing him in the face as he marched on and on, his feet carrying him to distant places he had never been before. A coldness swept across these foreign lands; it is something everyone who has been to war has experienced.

Of course, wars are frightening and no one likes them, but sometimes they can stop worse things from happening. This war lingered and lasted four years. You might have heard of it: people call it the First World War. Khudadad was one of about 400,000 Indian Muslim soldiers serving in the British Indian Army at the time. Unfortunately, many of these men did not make it back home, but Khudadad was one of the lucky ones. While he got hurt, he lived to tell his unbelievable tale about one icy and bitter cold day in October.

By then, Khudadad was no longer in France but had trekked miles and miles to neighbouring Belgium. He and his crew were on an important mission. They had to stop a huge group of German soldiers, who they were battling against, from reaching the coast. Europe's fate depended on infantrymen like him, so Khudadad dragged himself through squelchy fields and narrow ditches. His battered boots got soaked, his uniform was dirty, his body was sore and achy. Orders came in and he was sent straight to the ravaged frontlines near the Belgian town of Ypres, where all the fighting was happening.

Nothing could have prepared him for what he was about to witness. People were shooting and shouting at each other. Shells were pouring down like rain, bullet after bullet flying past Khudadad. He ducked down, trying to avoid the gunshots from the German soldiers, who easily outnumbered his regiment. It was difficult to stay together in these frantic moments of mayhem, and sure enough, his troop became cut off, leaving them vulnerable to attack.

The situation Khudadad suddenly found himself in was not only dangerous, it was life-threatening. Once the captain who commanded his unit was injured, Khudadad took charge. It takes a lot of courage to do that, and even when he was wounded, he did not give up. It is for this act of bravery that he is remembered today. Indian soldiers like Khudadad stopped the German advance that autumn, and he was the only man in his squad to survive that October day. When the horrid battle was over, he pretended to be dead, his worn face pressed into the mud, not daring to move as the German soldiers stomped past.

As night fell and it was safer to move, he sneaked through pitch-black fields to search for the rest of his regiment. His heart was thumping in his chest, and he was in pain. It could not have been easy, stumbling around in the darkness, these gloomy hours casting a long shadow over him. He needed to find his way to safety and track down his comrades, and somehow he did.

Soon after, he left for Britain, where he was treated at a hospital for wounded Indian soldiers. It took him a while to recover, and when he was feeling better, an unusual invitation arrived. Khudadad was asked to meet King George V! In Buckingham Palace! The king was also the last emperor of India, and on the day he met Khudadad – a man who had grown up on the other side of the world, a man who had risked everything for a country that was not his – he looked him up and down.

Emperors are used to people paying respect to them, but it was the king who honoured Khudadad by awarding him with the Victoria Cross, the highest British military medal. Not many have received this special medal for extreme bravery, and Khudadad was the first Indian to be given this award. He probably remembered this remarkable day – 26 January 1915 – for the rest of his life.

After the war, British Indian soldiers were largely forgotten, although they played a crucial role in history, helping to protect people and entire nations. That did not stop Khudadad from continuing to serve in the army until he became a subedar, the highest rank that Indian soldiers were permitted to reach. Many years later when he was living in Pakistan, another extraordinary thought popped into his head.

'Hm,' he said to himself. 'Maybe I should become a farmer after all.' And that is exactly what he did.

Today, Khudadad is remembered for his exceptional acts in the war. He showed the world that anyone can be brave – be it a soldier or a farmer. The medal didn't make him a hero. His selfless actions did.

GLOSSARY
British Indian Army – the main military force of the British Indian Empire before India became independent in 1947
Infantry – soldiers on foot
Regiment – a troop of soldiers

ILLUSTRATED BY ABEEHA TARIQ

BHIMRAO RAMJI AMBEDKAR

BY BALI RAI

My Baba (my father's father) looked wary as I filled our water bottle from the public fountain. We lived by the sea, in the city of Puri, on India's eastern coast. For many years our city's public water had been filthy and ridden with disease. Then our local government created a new system: fresh, clean, refreshing water from public fountains across the city. On a hot day, like today, this was very welcome indeed.

'**Please hurry,**' said Baba.

'**Why do you look so worried?**' I asked. '**We have all afternoon to complete our walk.**'

We took regular strolls around the city. The walks kept us both fit, and Baba was always pleased to see me. Yet, today he seemed anxious.

'**Some people might not like us taking water from this fountain,**' he replied.

'It is none of their business,' I told him. 'We may do as we please.'

Baba nodded. 'Perhaps now we can,' he said. 'But it wasn't always this way.'

'What do you mean?' I asked.

'We are born to a lowly caste,' he explained. 'We Dalits were once banned from using these public water fountains.'

I realized then why Baba was so anxious. India had a caste system. People were born into different castes, or classes, and some were assumed to be better than others. Dalits had once been seen as 'untouchables' – the lowest of all the people. Only, I was a child of modern India. My background would not prevent me from doing as I wished.

'Most young people no longer care about such things,' I said. 'The days of being outsiders is long past.'

Baba sighed and then nodded. 'Did I ever tell you about Bhimrao Ramji Ambedkar?'

He had, many times, but I did not say so. Baba loved to tell his story. And I wanted nothing more than for Baba to be happy.

'Bhimrao was a Dalit hero,' Baba added.

'I want to hear about him,' I replied.

Baba smiled as he began his tale.

*

Bhimrao was born in Madhya Pradesh, in Western India, in 1891. Like us, he was born a Dalit. His father was a subedar, and Bhimrao was the youngest of fourteen children. His early days were tough, as they were for all Dalits. At school, our children were not allowed to sit in classrooms. No matter what the weather, they were made to sit outside on special sacks, which they had to take home each day. The ground they sat on was seen as impure and was cleaned daily. Imagine that.

They were not allowed to touch the water jugs, nor the taps, in case the water became impure. When thirsty, Dalit children had to ask for water. The higher castes would stand over them and pour the water from above. It was an awful way to treat children. But that was just the way things were.

Bhimrao was a clever boy, and when his father retired, the family moved first to Satara and then Mumbai. Bhimrao was the only person from his village to graduate from high school, but life was still very hard. His mother died in 1896, and by 1907, nine of his siblings had died too. However, Bhimrao was determined to change his life for the better. He was able to study economics and politics at Mumbai University, which was very prestigious.

The Maharajah of Baroda was also studying at the university. The two became very good friends. The maharajah was a supporter of Dalit rights and wanted to end the injustices we faced. He was also very wealthy and supported Bhimrao's education. Thanks to the Maharajah, Bhimrao was able to study abroad. This was an exceptional opportunity for a Dalit – one that he was eager to take. In 1913, he went to New York's Columbia University to get his master's degree and a PhD. Afterwards, he moved to the London School of Economics. Bhimrao was an exceptionally gifted student. By moving abroad with the Maharajah's support, he gained opportunities that living in India would never have allowed. It was a huge moment for all Dalits – making one's life better through books and knowledge.

Unfortunately, the Europeans were at war – the Great War, they called it. Many of us Indians took part in the fighting, supporting Britain and her allies. Bhimrao could not continue his scholarship in wartime London. There was no money for such things. Instead, he came home and eventually taught at Sydenham College in Mumbai. Yet, even his excellent education and experience did not prevent discrimination. His fellow teachers looked down on Dalits. Bhimrao was still forbidden from using the water jugs, just as he had been as a child at school. It made him very angry and even more determined to change things for the better.

After the Great War, Bhimrao began to campaign for Dalits. He wanted our people to have equal rights and justice. In 1919, the British asked him to give evidence during an investigation. He also became friends with the Maharajah of Kolhapur, Shahu. Both men were opposed to discrimination, and they organized a conference led by Bhimrao. Shahu was impressed by Bhimrao's intelligence and his dedication to equality for Dalits. When Bhimrao began a Dalit newspaper, the *Mooknayak*, Shahu gave him a donation to help it succeed. The Maharajah also paid for Bhimrao to finish his scholarship in London.

Bhimrao did not stop campaigning after finishing his education. Instead, his campaigns grew bigger and bolder. Protests, conferences, marches – he did all of those things. In 1927, he organized our people in the city of Mahad. We Dalits were forbidden from touching the main water tank in the city. Bhimrao wanted to challenge that cruel injustice. When our people arrived at the tank, they were met with an armed and angry mob. Bhimrao did not want violence. He believed in democracy and peaceful protest, but our enemies did not care. Our people were beaten with sticks and insulted, but Bhimrao did not falter. It was a brave and rebellious act, and so important for our caste.

In 1932, we were given 148 seats in parliament. It was a huge day for us. It was the first time so-called untouchables were allowed to govern – to change laws, and make laws, and represent our own people. Such a thing seems normal now, but back then, it was rare. Bhimrao became the principle of a Mumbai college and published his most important book, *The Annihilation of Caste*. He helped to write India's first proper constitution and was our first law minister in 1947. He was tireless and determined, and never stopped fighting for our rights. He was a hero.

*

Baba was tearful by the time he finished his tale. We walked to the beach, sat in the sunshine and drank some water. The beach was packed with tourists, and the Bay of Bengal shimmered before us. A large brown cow sat on the sand, flicking its tale to ward off the flies. A holy man, one of a supposedly superior caste, stood in the sea and seemed to be praying.

'Bhimrao didn't remain a Hindu, did he?' I said.

Hinduism was the major religion in India. Our family were all Hindus.
'No,' said Baba. 'Bhimrao converted to Buddhism just before he died. He thought Hinduism would never accept equal rights for Dalits.'

'That must have been a brave decision,' I replied.

'It was,' said Baba. 'It led to thousands of our people doing the same thing.'

'How did he die?' I added.

'He was very ill with diabetes,' said Baba. 'He spent his final weeks unable to walk and then he passed away. It was 1956 – the year in which I was born.'

I nodded as I recalled pictures of Bhimrao's statue inside India's parliament. He had left behind a huge and important legacy.

Baba must have been thinking the same thing.

'The biggest part of his legacy,' he said, 'is to show young people that your caste cannot be allowed to define you. People will still do that, but if you believe in yourself, it matters little. Bhimrao was our greatest champion, my son. His struggles opened many doors for our people.'

'And our job,' I added. 'My job, is to keep those doors open and to keep fighting for what is right.'

Baba smiled.

'Exactly,' he said.

GLOSSARY

Great War – an alternative name for the First World War

Maharajah – the Sanskrit for 'great King', found in Hindi, Punjabi and many other Indian languages.

PhD – Doctor of Philosophy, the highest academic degree a person can achieve

Pradesh – 'province' or 'territory'. Similar to a county in the UK.

Subedar – a junior commissioned officer in the former British Indian Army

ILLUSTRATED BY JEN KHATUN

MARIA RESSA

BY SHAE DAVIES

'**N**anay, why is it called a sampaguita?' Maria asked her mother as she pressed the small white flower into the page of a book, closing it shut with a careful thud. The flower would soon dry, preserved like an old photograph.

'**Well, some say it is from the Arabian word "zanbaq", meaning jasmine.**' Her mother smiled, picking another one and tucking Maria's hair behind her ear so that she could slide the sleek stem of the flower atop it, like an accessory.

'**But legend says that once upon a time there lived a young princess named Lakambini. She met a prince and fell in love, and they promised their love would never end.**' Her mother paused to smile and touched Maria's chin.

'**Sumpa kita,**' she said. '**Or, in English?**'

'I promise you,' Maria responded.

'Correct! Sumpa kita symbolizes their undying love'

Maria smiled and looked out at the tiny white flowers.
'What happened to them?'

Maria's nanay took a deep breath and rubbed a thumb over a white petal.
'The prince left to find the princess's enemies, and sadly he never returned.'

'He died?' Maria asked. 'Like Tatay?'

'Yes.' Her mother nodded. 'And Lakambini died too – of a broken heart. She was buried on the hill where she and her prince made their promise. And you know what?'

Maria tilted her head in curiosity.

'And there on her grave, a flower grew. The sampaguita.'

Maria, older now, remembers the moment fondly. She remembers being a child running past the ruins of an old Spanish building, left to rot after the Philippines became independent from Spain in 1898. The building is now overgrown with sampaguita. How beautiful it is to see the national flower of the Philippines grow and grow and grow.

The sampaguita is believed to symbolize hope.

Just like Maria Ressa.

Maria cried on the aeroplane. Her ears hurt; they had popped as the plane shot up into the sky and hurtled into the clouds. The plane jostled back and forth roughly, and it felt like sitting inside a jeepney on a bumpy stretch of road. Except there were no sounds of noisy beeps and chatter, just the low hum of the plane's engine and the distant mumble of prayers in Tagalog, as titas rocked gently back and forth clutching rosaries.

'Ateh, are they praying because we are going to crash and die?' Mary Jane asked her big sister, her tiny voice very serious and her eyes wide with worry.

Maria smiled and took her hand. She was a sweet girl with eyes that always searched for the truth and a voice that always spoke it.

After a long pause, she said, **'Maybe,'** and went back to looking out the window.

Mary Jane started to cry and Maria felt bad, but she did not like to lie. The truth was important to her, and truthfully, the plane shook so violently that she was scared too.

Maria looked over at Mummy, who had fallen asleep. Mummy had moved to America years ago and she came back for them, just like she promised. Maria thought of how much she would miss the warmth of the Philippines and the warmth of its people. She thought of how much she missed her tatay.

'You can't believe everything you see and hear,' her dad would always say. **'You must look for the truth, anak, for yourself – always.'** And he'd shake a finger at her. She always knew something he said was serious when he shook a finger while saying it.

The truth was important to Maria. Even when Mary Jane would say it was Maria who ate all the sticky dried mango, Maria would huff and puff until her sister would admit it was a lie.

Maria dreamed of a world where people would not lie – not just about sticky mango, but about things that really mattered. Big or small, the truth was important, and people should know it. Maria carried this with her always.

With a bumpy bang, the big plane landed safely. As soon as it did, everyone clapped their hands and hurried passengers started to stand. But Maria stayed still. Her eyes were glued to the small oval window next to her. Tiny white flakes blew quickly past, some of them drifting towards the glass and sticking to it.

'Snow,' Mummy said in English, with a smile, watching Maria's eyes take it in. Snow. Maria repeated the word in her head. This was the first time she had ever seen snow, and she thought it was beautiful.

Outside, the air was a cold she had never felt, and Maria smiled as snowflakes landed on her cheek and nose, melting and disappearing, leaving behind a faint tingle, like a kiss.

Aged ten, Maria stepped off the plane and into Toms River, New Jersey, where she lived with her mother and her stepfather, from whom she took the name **'Ressa'.**

Maria studied hard, learning English alongside her schoolwork. She was passionate about music and learned how to play eight different musical instruments, from piano to glockenspiel, which she only learned how to play because she thought it sounded like a funny word.

Then one day, all her hard work paid off and Maria went to study English at Princeton University.

In 1986 Maria graduated and went back to the Philippines, with a Fulbright Fellowship. She studied political theatre at the University of the Philippines and earned herself a master's degree in journalism.

Not long after, in 1988 Maria became the Manila bureau chief at CNN (a huge TV channel!) and was the network's lead investigative reporter in Asia for the next seventeen years. During this time, Maria covered every major news story in Asia, including news on terrorism. Maria bravely pursued terror groups in Southeast Asia. Because of her investigation into the Moro Islamic Liberation Front, she was the first to link the group to al-Qaeda (a dangerous group of people.).

Maria's success did not stop there. She started a Facebook page called MovePH with a group of other Filipino journalists. In 2012, this page became an online news website named Rappler. Now they have more than 4.5 million followers on Facebook!

RAPPLER

The name itself comes from the root words **'rap'** (to discuss) and **'ripple'** (to make waves). This is exactly what Rappler did!

Based in Pasig, Metro Manila, Rappler became a community of action.

Maria was inspired to create Rappler by the **'People Power'** movement – when crowds of ordinary people took to the streets of Manila to overthrow the horrible dictator Ferdinand Marcos in 1986.

Rappler has also shown the world the truth about the violent government of Rodrigo Duterte (president of the Philippines). He scared other journalists into keeping quiet, and everyone had been afraid to speak out – everyone except Maria Ressa and Rappler!

Maria wanted to show others how important truthful journalism is. She taught courses on politics and the press in Southeast Asia for Princeton University and on broadcast journalism for the University of the Philippines. Maria also worked with Google and Facebook to help make sure their systems did not twist information or help governments spread disinformation.

*

'What is disinformation?' a girl in her class asked Maria.

'It is false information. Lies! Spread to trick people.'

Heads around the room nodded in understanding.

'Duterte uses disinformation on social media like a weapon!' Maria spoke with passion. **'He uses it to scare and silence all that stand against him. He twists the public's understanding of reality.'**

'I heard that he created fake Facebook accounts,' another student said.

'Yes! He used fake accounts to feed disinformation to people, to drown

out the facts. **He did this to change how people see and to make them behave how he wants.'** She shook her head.

'Disinformation is Duterte's weapon.' Maria paused and looked into the eyes of those around her. **'But truth – truth is our weapon.'**

As Maria finished speaking, a man arrived with a large envelope. She did not even need to look at it, she already knew what it was. Maria was being sued, again.

The Filipino government have targeted Maria because they are angry that she is showing the world the truth. She has been sued and arrested multiple times. In 2020, a Filipino court convicted Maria for a newly invented crime called **'cyber libel'.**

Maria faced years in prison! But she fought for her freedom and did not let them silence her, like they had done to so many others.

In 2018 Maria was *Time* magazine's Person of the Year, and in 2021 Maria became the first Filipino journalist to be awarded the Nobel Peace Prize. This is a symbol of the fairer and more honest future she fights for, and a symbol that brings hope to the nation.

Just like the sampaguita.
Just like Maria Ressa.

GLOSSARY

Ateh – older sister

Anak – child

Bureau chief – a type of journalist who often works in locations far from the newspaper's base of operations

Cyber libel – a term used when someone has posted on the Internet or emailed something that is untrue and damaging about someone else

Dictator – a ruler with total power over a country, typically one who has obtained control by force

Jeepney – a Filipino bus

Journalism – the activity or profession of writing for newspapers, magazines or news websites or preparing news to be broadcast.

Fulbright Fellowship – a scholarship that pays for students to go abroad for research or study

Nanay – mum

Nobel Peace Prize – an award given every year for outstanding achievement in the fields of physics, chemistry, medicine or physiology, literature and economics

Sampaguita – national flower of the Philippines

Tatay – dad

Tagalog – main language of the Philippines

Terrorism – the unlawful use of violence and intimidation, especially against civilians, in the pursuit of political aim

Tita – auntie

ILLUSTRATED BY GINNIE HSU

ABOUT
THE AUTHORS

SUFIYA AHMED

Sufiya was born in India and arrived in the UK as a baby. She worked in advertising and in the House of Commons before becoming a full-time author. In 2010 Sufiya set up the BIBI Foundation, a non-profit organization, to arrange visits to the Houses of Parliament for diverse and underprivileged school children.

MAISIE CHAN

Maisie is a British Chinese children's author from Birmingham. She loves dim sum, yoga and travelling. She runs Bubble Tea Writers Network to support and encourage writers of East and Southeast Asian (ESEA) descent in the U.K. She has a dog called Miko who has big eyes. She lives in Glasgow with her family.

SHAE DAVIES

Shae Davies is a half-Filipino, half-Welsh writer from South-East London. She is the Marketing and Brand Executive for OWN IT! – a storytelling lifestyle brand, publishing and producing powerful stories across books, music, art and film. She is passionate about finding and encouraging a new generation of exciting creatives, coming from a creative background herself as a poet and a freelance professional bid and tender writer.

SAIMA MIR

Saima is an award-winning writer and journalist. She is a recipient of the Commonwealth Broadcast Association's World View Award, and has written for numerous publications including The Times and The Independent. Saima's essay for *It's Not About The Burqa* appeared in *Guardian Weekend* and received over 250,000 hits over two days. Her debut novel *The Khan* was a Times Crime Novel of the Year.

BALI RAI

Bali has been writing short stories and poetry since the age of eight. As a child he made up wild and exciting stories and his imagination has been vivid ever since.

ANNABELLE SAMI

Annabelle is a writer, director and performer. It was whilst reading children's books when babysitting that she realized there was a lack of representation of funny girls and diverse characters in children's books – and she decided to do something about it. Growing up mixed-race, she never found her own life reflected in a book and now it's her mission to make sure that every spirited, witty and adventurous girl has her own special book that she can relate to.

REBEKA SHAID

Rebeka was raised in a multicultural household, surrounded by piles of books, nosy siblings, and lots of mythical trees that are known as the Black Forest. Growing up she wanted to be a snake charmer or ventriloquist, but that (luckily) didn't pan out. Instead, she turned to words and writing. In her writing, she likes to explore themes of identity, loss, and coming of age.

CYNTHIA SO

Cynthia was born in Hong Kong and lives in London. When they're not writing, they can often be found at the theatre, entranced by a play or a musical. They're also extremely enthusiastic about board games and tabletop role-playing.

REKHA WAHEED

Rekha Waheed is British Bengali author from London. She is the author of *The A–Z Guide to Arranged Marriage*, *My Bollywood Wedding* and *Saris and the City*. She has written for Monsoon Press and Hachette/Headline Publishing Group imprint Little Black Dress. Rekha ran Harrow Writers Club for emerging writers and loves travelling, tennis and plenty of coffee with lots of cake. Rekha continues to live in London with her beloved family.

ABOUT THE ILLUSTRATORS

AALIYA JALEEL

Aaliya is a Sri Lankan–American illustrator who loves illustrating bright, pastel colour palettes and floral themes. Some of her past works include the books *Under My Hijab and Muslim Girls Rise*. In addition to being an illustrator, Aaliya works as a designer for animation. When she's not drawing, she enjoys exploring Dallas, USA and hunting for new dessert spots with her friends.

AMANDA YOSHIDA

Amanda attended Gnomon School of Visual Effects in Los Angeles, USA and went on to work for several years as a 3D artist and graphic designer. When she's not illustrating or playing with her energetic kiddo (aka – the "little spider monkey"), she enjoys connecting with her Asian and Irish heritage through art, storytelling, sushi and the occasional Irish coffee.

DEBBY RAHMALIA

Debby is an illustrator and storyteller based in Indonesia. She graduated from Bandung Institute of Technology, where she earned a Bachelor of Interior Design degree. Debby is continually looking for opportunities to illustrate great stories with the desire to see how her work will impact young minds.

GINNIE HSU

Ginnie Hsu is an illustrator, designer, animator, maker and educator living in upstate New York, USA where she teaches illustration at the University of Syracuse. Her love for drawing began in her childhood in Taiwan. Her work is often inspired by everyday life, nature, human living, travel and old artefacts she randomly finds.

HANNAH LI

Hannah is a Chinese illustrator based in Manhattan, New York, USA. She started drawing when she was a kid, you would have often found little Hannah amuse herself by doodling. After receiving a Bachelor's Degree in Fine Arts in China, she moved to the USA and pursued her MFA in illustration at Savannah College of Art and Design.

JEN KHATUN

Jen Khatun is a published children's book illustrator of Bangladeshi/Indian heritage, who grew up in the beautiful quaint city of Winchester, UK. She has had the great delight to have published work with: Cantata Learning Books, Bramble Kids Books, Lantana Publishing, Macmillan Children's Books, Oxford University Press and Walker Books.

JOCELYN KAO

Jocelyn Kao is an illustrator from Taiwan and currently based in Montréal, Canada. She graduated from Academy of Art University in San Francisco, and worked as a concept artist in animation and game for seven years. Jocelyn had published her first picture book *Chacha à Paris* in France in 2015, and the second book *Chacha à Tokyo* has won a merit award of iJungle illustration competition in 2020.

KÜBRA TEBER

Kübra is an illustrator living in Istanbul, Turkey. After she finished her design education in Interior Design Department of Mimar Sinan Fine Arts University, she started making drawings in order to be a part of the children's stories which she had read as a child with great pleasure.

TIKA AND TATA

Tika and Tata Bobokhidze are sisters from Georgia, with a passion for drawing since childhood. Their illustration style is versatile and includes many different techniques that follow messages and feelings that they want to express through their work. They love to draw nature, animals and plants in various colours and styles. Usually, their work combines digital medium and hand-drawn textures and contours.

INDEX